FORCED OSCILLATIONS IN NON-LINEAR SYSTEMS

FORCED OSCILLATIONS
IN
NON-LINEAR SYSTEMS

BY

CHIHIRO HAYASHI, D.Sc., D.Eng.

Professor of Electrical Engineering, Kyoto University
Formerly, Research Engineer, Mitsubishi Electric
and Manufacturing Company

FIRST EDITION

OSAKA, JAPAN
NIPPON PRINTING AND PUBLISHING COMPANY, LTD.
1953

NIPPON PRINTING AND PUBLISHING COMPANY, LTD.
KIKKO–CHO 2, FUKUSHIMA–KU, OSAKA, JAPAN

AGENT OUTSIDE JAPAN
CHARLES E. TUTTLE COMPANY
RUTLAND, VERMONT, U.S.A.

PRINTED IN JAPAN

TO MY TEACHER:

RISABURO TORIKAI
TO WHOM THE INSPIRATION FOR THIS
BOOK IS LARGELY DUE

INTRODUCTION

The purpose of this book is to provide engineers and physicists with practical knowledge concerning the important subject of non-linear oscillations. It should at first be mentioned that the problems discussed in this book are rather limited to a small segment of the general field of non-linear mechanics, i. e., the field of forced oscillations; furthermore, throughout the text, only those with one degree of freedom are treated. However, a wide variety of oscillations may still occur in those systems under the influence of external forces.

Basically all the problems in mechanics are non-linear from the outset, and the linearizations commonly practised are approximating devices, and they are good enough or quite satisfactory for most purposes. However, there are also many cases in which linear treatments may not be applied at all. Frequently, essentially new phenomena occur in non-linear systems which cannot, in principle, occur in linear systems. The principal aim of this book is not to introduce methods of improving the accuracy obtainable by linearization, but rather to focus attention on those features of the problems in which the non-linearity results in distinctive new phenomena. In writing this book, the author has wished to present the underlying principle and theory in such a way that they are of use to readers whose primary interest lies in applying these ideas and methods to concrete physical problems. The author has therefore laid more stress on manifesting the intimate relationship between the analysis and experiments. Practically, in so far as is discussed in this book, the analytical results have shown good agreement with experimental facts. The author has not aimed at delivering a rigorous mathematical treatment of non-linear differential equations. Therefore, from the mathematical point of view, there will be some points open to discussion in proving the validity, particularly in the case when the departure from linearity is not small. Although this book is not addressed in any sense to the pure mathematicians, it will be the author's pleasure if the results in this book attract the attention of mathematicians so that he could expect more rigorous justification of the analysis.

Before outlining the actual contents of the book, it should be mentioned that the author has read with interest the recent literature in this field; the books by Minorsky [47],* Andronow and Chaikin [38], Stoker [51], and McLachlan [46] especially affording him much information. However, the whole of the present

---

* Numbers in parentheses indicate references on pp. 153-155.

manuscript was prepared before 1948, independently of the progress in such foreign countries. Furthermore, the author has limited the subject of investigation to forced oscillations only, and so the analysis and experimental results are more detailed in many places as compared with those in the books mentioned above. These facts have stimulated the author to write this book.

The basic mathematical idea in this book is due to the works of Poincaré [48], Bendixson [3], and Liapounoff [19, 42]. The technique applied is also due to Rayleigh [49], van der Pol [27–30], Duffing [39], Mandelstam and Papalexi [21], and Andronow and Witt [1]. It is the author's regret that time did not allow him to refer to the recent progress in non-linear oscillations [41]. †

The text is divided into two parts. Part I consists of four chapters and is devoted to the study of non-linear periodic oscillations in steady states. Particular attention is directed to the stability investigation of equilibrium states by applying Mathieu's or Hill's equation as a stability criterion. Part II consists of two chapters and is concerned with the transient states of oscillations which, with the lapse of time, lead to the periodic states mentioned above. The geometrical or topological analyses of Poincaré and Bendixson answer this purpose. Six appendices to the text complement the methods of analyses and experiments.

In Chapter I, the salient features of the non-linear oscillations are first mentioned and then the stability of the periodic oscillation is discussed by solving a variational equation which characterizes small variations from the periodic states of equilibrium. This variational equation leads to a linear equation in which the coefficient is periodic in time. If all solutions of this equation are bounded, the oscillation is stable, otherwise it is unstable. In order to establish the stability criterion, the characteristic exponents for the unbounded solutions are calculated by Whittaker's method [36, 53]. Then the generalized stability condition is derived by comparing the characteristic exponents with the damping of the system under consideration. This condition secures the stability not only of the oscillation having the fundamental frequency (of the periodic oscillation), but also of the oscillations with harmonic frequencies. Hence, the generalized stability condition obtained in this way is particularly effective in studying the oscillations in which higher harmonics are excited.

The three chapters that follow are devoted to the investigation of different types of periodic oscillation. Chapter II treats the harmonic oscillations in which the fundamental component having the same frequency as that of the external force predominates over the higher harmonics. The non-linearity is

---

† Dr. M. L. Cartwright has kindly sent him some of her recent papers [4].

provided with the symmetrical and unsymmetrical characteristics. In Chapter III the higher harmonic oscillations in series-oscillation systems are first studied. This becomes a matter of discussion in the case when the external force is very large. The self-excitation of the higher harmonic oscillations in parallel-oscillation systems is also discussed. Chapter IV deals with the subharmonic oscillations in which the smallest period of the oscillations is an integral multiple of the period of the external force. The relationship between the non-linear characteristics and the order of the subharmonics is first discussed. Then the subharmonic oscillation of order 1/3 and that of order 1/2 are investigated at full length.

For each oscillation mentioned above, the stability condition derived in Chapter I is applied to ascertain the stability of the equilibrium state. This condition is particularly effective in investigating the stability problems of the higher harmonic and the subharmonic oscillations. Experimental investigations are also carried out by making use of electrical oscillatory circuits which contain saturable iron-core inductance as the non-linear element; and satisfactory agreement between the theoretical analysis and the experimental results is found in the respective cases.

Part II is devoted to the investigation of non-linear oscillations in transient states. The differential equations which govern the oscillations are, under some restrictions, transformed to the following equation of the first order:

$$dy/dx = Y(x, y)/X(x, y),$$

and the integral curves of this equation are studied following Poincaré [48] and Bendixson [3] with the basic idea that the singularities of the above equation are correlated with the periodic steady states and its integral curves with the transient states.

The main advantage of this geometrical or topological method lies in the fact that it is not confined to the analysis of the non-linear oscillations with particular initial conditions, but it gives, so to speak, a bird's eye view of the totality of oscillations of different types which may arise in a given system under all possible conditions.*

In Chapter V are treated the transient states of the harmonic oscillations by means of geometrical discussion of the integral curves. Further, the stability of non-linear oscillations in equilibrium states is investigated in detail by the

---

* It should be mentioned, however, that the discussion is usually limited to the two-dimensional case.

topological analysis of integral curves in the neighborhood of the singularities. The limit cycle correlated with a quasi-periodic oscillation is also discussed concerning a system in which the damping and the restoring force are both non-linear.

Chapter VI treats the transient states of the subharmonic oscillation. Although only the case of the oscillation of order 1/3 is discussed, the method of analysis may also be applied to the oscillation of other orders. In those two chapters, V and VI, the regions of initial conditions which give rise to the different types of oscillations are theoretically determined. Some experiments using the electrical oscillatory circuits are also performed to confirm the pertinence of the approximation applied in the foregoing analysis, and satisfactory agreement is found between them.

As has been mentioned earlier, six appendices are annexed to the text. Appendix I gives expansions of the Mathieu functions ce_1, se_1, $\cdots$, ce_3, se_3. Appendix II shows the unstable solutions of Hill's equation computed by making use of Whittaker's method, and Appendix III deals with the extended form of Hill's equation. In Appendix IV the stability condition is compared with one of those derived by Mandelstam and Papalexi [21] for the subharmonic oscillations. Appendix V gives complementary remarks concerning integral curves and singular points which are frequently referred to in the analysis in Part II. Finally in Appendix VI is shown the circuit diagram of the electronic switch which is used in the experiments, and the sequence of operation is explained in detail.

ACKNOWLEDGMENTS

The writing of this book was greatly facilitated by the Grant in Aid for Publishing Research Result of the Ministry of Education of Japan and the generous support of the Mitsubishi Electric Mfg. Company.

The starting point of this book was the author's two dissertations on non-linear oscillations submitted to the Faculty of Engineering in 1942 and to the Faculty of Science in 1948 under the guidance of Dr. R. Torikai, former President of the Kyoto University. The author wishes particularly to acknowledge his indebtedness to him in promoting this investigation. The author's thanks are also due to Professor Emeritus T. Okamoto and Professor T. Matsumoto both of the Kyoto University, to Mr. M. Hori, former Director of the Research Laboratories, Mitsubishi Electric Mfg. Company, and particularly to Professor R. Rüdenberg of the Harvard University for his suggestion to publish this book in English.

In the preparation of the present book the author was greatly aided by Professor S. Tomotika and by Assistant Professor H. Nishihara who gave him valuable suggestions and much good advice of all kinds. The author is likewise grateful to Messrs. H. Takatsuki, M. Kuwahara, and S. Toki for carrying out a great deal of tedious computations. The author wishes also to express his appreciation of the assistance he received from Mr. Kuwahara for cooperation in drawing and proof-reading.

In presenting this volume the author wishes to acknowledge the help he has received from the staffs of the Ministry of Education, and from Mr. S. Kobayashi, President of the Nippon Printing and Publishing Company. In this connection the author also tender his best thanks to Messrs. A. Hirosaki and T. Ishikawa both of the Mitsubishi Electric Mfg. Company, and to Mr. F. Shimoda, President of the Mitsubishi Paper Mills Ltd.

This book is dedicated to Dr. Torikai as a token of esteem and gratefulness, and as an acknowledgment of the strong influence he has had in the author's scientific development.

Kyoto University, Kyoto, Japan   Chihiro Hayashi
      December, 1952

CONTENTS

PART I

NON-LINEAR OSCILLATIONS IN STEADY STATES

CHAPTER I

STABILITY OF PERIODIC OSCILLATIONS

1. Manifoldness of periodic oscillations in non-linear systems

When a periodic force is applied to a linear system, the resulting motion is obtained by a superposition of the transient- and the steady-state components of oscillations. The former is due to the free oscillation of the system, while the latter is related to the forced oscillation which arises from the action of the external force. Since the free oscillation is damped out after a sufficiently long period of time, only the forced oscillation having the same frequency as that of the external force would be observed. Thus, as far as linear systems are concerned, the forced oscillation is uniquely determined once the system and the external force are given, and is by no means affected by the initial condition with which the oscillation was started. In non-linear systems, however, the circumstances may be quite different in this respect. The theorem of superposition will no longer apply in this case. We shall see later that non-linear systems can possess a wide variety of periodic oscillations in addition to those which have the same period as the external force. It has been pointed out by Trefftz [33] that if the solution of a differential equation

$$\frac{d^2v}{d\tau^2} = F\left(v, \frac{dv}{d\tau}, \tau\right),$$

with

$$F\left(v, \frac{dv}{d\tau}, \tau + T\right) = F\left(v, \frac{dv}{d\tau}, \tau\right)$$

$$(1.1)$$

is stable, it must finally lead to a periodic solution in which the least period is equal to the period T of the external force, or equal to an integral multiple (different from unity) of T. Corresponding to these two cases the terms "harmonic" and "subharmonic" oscillations are respectively applied.

In the following sections we confine our attention to the stability problem of periodic solutions which are either harmonic or subharmonic even if higher harmonics may predominate. It is known from the theory of differential equations that equation (1.1) possesses such solution $v(\tau)$ that is uniquely determined once the values of $v(0)$ and $(dv/d\tau)_{\tau=0}$, i. e., the initial conditions, are prescribed. It is, however, the distinctive character of non-linear oscillations that the various types of periodic solutions of (1.1) may exist for a particular system with different values of the initial conditions. One of our experimental results is illustrated in Fig. 1.1. The oscillogram shows the wave forms of the applied voltage (60 c. p. s.) and the resulting currents in an electrical circuit with a saturable iron-core inductance and a capacitance in series. Applying the same voltage (a), we see that three types of oscillation, i. e., (b), (c), and (d), are obtained by varying only the amount of the initial charge across the condenser.

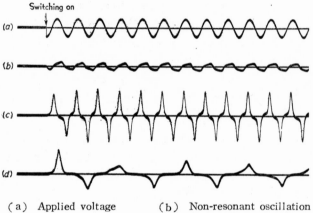

(a) Applied voltage   (b) Non-resonant oscillation
(c) Resonant oscillation   (d) Subharmonic oscillation

Fig. 1. 1. Different types of oscillation in a non-linear system.

Contrary to many cases of linear differential equations, it is hardly possible to find the general solution of (1.1) for the given initial conditions. Moreover, since explicit solutions in terms of the elementary functions are not to be expected, the differential equation (1.1) is treated by various analytic approximation methods. As mentioned above, in so far as we deal with the periodic solutions, our conventional method of solution is to assume for $v(\tau)$ a Fourier series development with undetermined coefficients, and then to fix them by the non-linear relations obtained by substituting the series into the original equation (1.1). It should, however, be noticed that this method of solution is merely to find out the periodic states of equilibrium, which are not always sustained, but are only able to last so long as they are stable. The circumstances under which this condition obtains are determined by a further stability investigation.

2. Stability of periodic states of equilibrium [11]

A state of equilibrium is said to be stable or unstable according as whether any variation from this state caused by any sufficiently small perturbation attenuates or not with the lapse of time. As a typical case of equation (1.1), we now consider the following non-linear differential equation, i. e.,

$$\frac{d^2v}{d\tau^2}+f(v)\frac{dv}{d\tau}+g(v)=e(\tau),$$

with

$$e(\tau+T)=e(\tau).$$

$$(2.1)$$

Let the periodic solution of (2.1) be expressed by

$$v(\tau)=\Phi(\tau),\tag{2.2}$$

in which the least period is equal to the period T of the external force, or equal to an integral multiple of T. If the small variation from this periodic state is denoted by ξ, we obtain the following variational equation for ξ by the substitution of $v(\tau)+\xi$ in place of $v(\tau)$; i. e.,

$$\frac{d^2\xi}{d\tau^2}+f(v)\frac{d\xi}{d\tau}+\left[\frac{df}{d\tau}+\frac{dg}{dv}\right]\xi=0,\tag{2.3}$$

or

$$\frac{d^2\xi}{d\tau^2}+F(\tau)\frac{d\xi}{d\tau}+G(\tau)\xi=0,\tag{2.4}$$

in which $F(\tau)$ and $G(\tau)$ are periodic functions of τ, determined by the substitution of (2.2) into (2.3). Now, introducing a new variable η with the following relation:

$$\xi=\exp\left[-\frac{1}{2}\int F(\tau)\,d\tau\right]\cdot\eta,\tag{2.5}$$

equation (2.4) is transformed to

$$\frac{d^2\eta}{d\tau^2}+\left[G(\tau)-\frac{1}{2}\frac{dF}{d\tau}-\frac{1}{4}\left\{F(\tau)\right\}^2\right]\eta=0.\tag{2.6}$$

This is a linear equation in which the coefficient of η is a periodic function of τ and may be developed into a Fourier series.

By Floquet's theory [5] the general solution of (2.6) is given by

$$\eta=c_1e^{\mu\tau}\phi(\tau)+c_2e^{-\mu\tau}\psi(\tau),\tag{2.7}$$

where c_1, c_2 are arbitrary constants, μ is a number (usually called the *characteristic exponent*) dependent upon the coefficients of the Fourier series in (2.6), and $\phi(\tau)$, $\psi(\tau)$ are periodic functions in τ whose period is the same as or twice the period of the Fourier series.

Now we turn to the present stability investigation. As one readily sees from (2.5) and (2.7), the variation ξ tends to zero with the increase of τ if the real part of $-\frac{1}{2}F_0 \pm \mu$ is negative, where F_0 is the constant term in the series of $F(\tau)$; and the corresponding periodic state of equilibrium will be stable. On the contrary, if the real part of $-\frac{1}{2}F_0 \pm \mu$ is positive, the variation ξ diverges without limit with the increase of τ, and the corresponding periodic state is unstable. Hence, for establishing the stability criterion, it is necessary to evaluate the characteristic exponent μ in (2.7). Therefore, some representative equations of the form (2.6) will be discussed in the following sections.

3.1. Mathieu's equation [18, 22, 44, 45, 52, 53]

We commence with Mathieu's equation, since it constitutes a suitable introduction to our later consideration. The equation takes the form

$$\frac{d^2x}{d\tau^2} + (a + 16q \cos 2\tau)\, x = 0, \tag{3.1}$$

where the parameters a, q will be limited to real numbers. The equation is a particular case of a linear type of the second order with periodic coefficients. Thus Floquet's theory applies, and a particular solution of (3.1) is given by

$$x = e^{\mu\tau}\phi(\tau), \tag{3.2}$$

where μ is the characteristic exponent dependent upon the parameters a, q, and $\phi(\tau)$ is a periodic function of τ with period π or 2π. Since (3.1) is unchanged if $-\tau$ be written for τ, $e^{-\mu\tau}\phi(-\tau)$ is another independent solution. Hence, the general solution of (3.1) may be expressed by

$$x = c_1 e^{\mu\tau}\phi(\tau) + c_2 e^{-\mu\tau}\phi(-\tau), \tag{3.3}$$

c_1 and c_2 being arbitrary constants.

We shall now discuss the stability of solutions for real values of τ, and the following cases will be considered with the increase of τ;

(a) a solution is defined to be unstable if it tends to $\pm\infty$ as $\tau \to +\infty$,

(b) a solution is defined to be stable if it tends to zero or remains bounded as $\tau \to +\infty$,

(c) a solution with period π or 2π is said to be neutral, but may be regarded as a special case of a stable solution.

In equation (3.3), since $\phi(\tau)$ and $\phi(-\tau)$ are periodic in τ, the stability depends upon $e^{\mu\tau}$, or upon μ. Taking the form of solution (3.3) where $\phi(\tau)$ has the period π or 2π, the characteristic exponent μ may be considered to be real or imaginary, but not complex. Hence the solution (3.3) is unstable if μ is real, and stable if μ is imaginary.

3.2. Mathieu functions and correlated characteristic numbers of the parameters [6, 44, 45, 52, 53]

We shall consider the case (c) in Section 3.1, i.e., the periodic solutions of (3.1) with period π or 2π. These solutions are, by definition, called the *Mathieu functions*. In order that such solutions may exist, a must have one of an infinite sequence of values for each value of q; that is, a must be one of an infinite sequence of functions of q. When q is zero, the solutions required are 1, $\cos\tau$, $\sin\tau$, $\cos 2\tau$, $\sin 2\tau$, and so on; the corresponding values of a are the squares of the integers. For other values of q, the Mathieu functions are denoted by $ce_0(\tau, q)$, $ce_1(\tau, q)$, $se_1(\tau, q)$, $ce_2(\tau, q)$, $se_2(\tau, q)$, etc. $ce_n(\tau, q)$ and $se_n(\tau, q)$ are those Mathieu functions that reduce respectively to $\cos nx$ and $\sin nx$ when $q \to 0$.

The Fourier series for the Mathieu functions are preferably written in the forms

$$
\left.
\begin{aligned}
ce_{2n}(\tau, q) &= \sum_{r=0}^{\infty} A_{2r}(q) \cos 2r\tau , \\[2mm]
ce_{2n+1}(\tau, q) &= \sum_{r=0}^{\infty} A_{2r+1}(q) \cos(2r+1)\tau , \\[2mm]
se_{2n}(\tau, q) &= \sum_{r=1}^{\infty} B_{2r}(q) \sin 2r\tau , \\[2mm]
se_{2n+1}(\tau, q) &= \sum_{r=0}^{\infty} B_{2r+1}(q) \sin(2r+1)\tau .
\end{aligned}
\right\} \qquad (3.4)
$$

In these series A, B are functions of q. If $|q|$ is sufficiently small, these coefficients and accordingly the Mathieu functions are developed as the power series of q.* For a given q, the value of a is definite for each Mathieu function, and is called the *characteristic number* of the corresponding Mathieu function

---

* Very little is known on the convergence of series for the Mathieu functions. Only for $ce_0(\tau, q)$, Watson [35] has shown that the series converges when $32|q^2| < 1$, by constructing a *fonction majorante* for the coefficient of the series.

[16]. Denoting, in general, the characteristic numbers by a_{cn} and a_{sn} corresponding to $ce_n(\tau, q)$ and $se_n(\tau, q)$ respectively, we have the following expansions.

$$a_{c1} = 1 - 8q - 8q^2 + 8q^3 - \frac{8}{3}q^4 + \cdots,$$

$$a_{s1} = 1 + 8q - 8q^2 - 8q^3 - \frac{8}{3}q^4 + \cdots,$$

$$a_{c2} = 4 + \frac{80}{3}q^2 - \frac{6104}{27}q^4 + \cdots,$$

$$a_{s2} = 4 - \frac{16}{3}q^2 + \frac{40}{27}q^4 + \cdots,$$

$$a_{c3} = 9 + 4q^2 - 8q^3 + \frac{13}{5}q^4 + \cdots,$$

$$a_{s3} = 9 + 4q^2 + 8q^3 + \frac{13}{5}q^4 + \cdots,$$

$$\cdots\cdots\cdots\cdots\cdots .$$

(3.5)

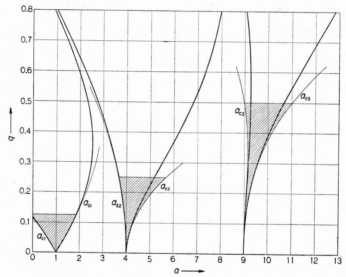

Fig. 3.1. Stability chart for Mathieu's equation.

Tables of the Mathieu functions $ce_0(\tau, q), \cdots, ce_5(\tau, q)$; $se_1(\tau, q), \cdots,$ $se_6(\tau, q)$ and the corresponding characteristic numbers are computed by Ince [16, 17] for the range of $q = 0$ to 1.25.† The characteristic curves showing the relation between q and a_{cn}, a_{sn} ($n = 1, 2, 3$) are plotted in Fig. 3.1, where the

---

† See also Reference [43].

thick-line curves are plotted from the tables and the fine-line curves are calculated by equations (3.5). These characteristic curves divide the plane into regions of stability and instability, that is, when a point (a, q) lies on the unstable region interposed between a_{cn} and a_{sn}, the original equation (3.1) has an unstable solution, and when a point (a, q) lies on the remaining region, a stable solution results.

3.3. Solutions in the unstable regions

As we have already mentioned in Section 2, the stability problem of the states of equilibrium in dissipative systems is investigated by computing the characteristic exponent of the unstable solution of equation (2.6). In order to solve such an equation, the method by Hill's infinite determinant [13] and many others are proposed, among which the one introduced by Whittaker [36, 53] is expedient in finding the unstable solution when $|q|$ is small.

Following Whittaker we shall first find the unstable solution associated with the first unstable region interposed between a_{c1} and a_{s1} in Fig. 3.1. As shown in equation (3.5), if the parameters a and q satisfy the relation

$$a = a_{c1} = 1 - 8q - 8q^2 + 8q^3 + \cdots ,$$

equation (3.1) has a solution (see Appendix I)

$$x = ce_1 (\tau, q) = \cos \tau + q \cos 3\tau + q^2 \left(- \cos 3\tau + \frac{1}{3} \cos 5\tau \right)$$

$$+ q^3 \left(\frac{1}{3} \cos 3\tau - \frac{4}{9} \cos 5\tau + \frac{1}{18} \cos 7\tau \right) + \cdots ,$$

and if

$$a = a_{s1} = 1 + 8q - 8q^2 - 8q^3 + \cdots ,$$

then

$$x = se_1 (\tau, q) = \sin \tau + q \sin 3\tau + q^2 \left(\sin 3\tau + \frac{1}{3} \sin 5\tau \right)$$

$$+ q^3 \left(\frac{1}{3} \sin 3\tau + \frac{4}{9} \sin 5\tau + \frac{1}{18} \sin 7\tau \right) + \cdots .$$

Whittaker has pointed out that they are degenerate cases of a quasi-periodic solution of Mathieu's equation, having the form

$$x = e^{\mu \tau} \cdot \phi(\tau) ,$$

where

$$\phi(\tau) = \sin (\tau - \sigma) + a_3 \cos (3\tau - \sigma) + b_3 \sin (3\tau - \sigma)$$
$$+ a_5 \cos (5\tau - \sigma) + b_5 \sin (5\tau - \sigma) + \cdots ,$$

(3.6)

where σ is a new parameter taking a value between 0 and $-\pi/2$ for the unstable solution. Hence, the Mathieu functions $ce_1(\tau, q)$ and $se_1(\tau, q)$ are simply particular cases corresponding to $\sigma = -\pi/2$ and 0 respectively. The characteristic exponent μ and the unknown coefficients a_3, b_3, $\cdots$ in equation (3.6) are determined as follows. Since a, q and μ, σ are interrelated, we may assume, for small values of $|q|$, that

$$\left.\begin{aligned}
\mu &= q\kappa(\sigma)+q^2\lambda(\sigma)+q^3\mu(\sigma)+\cdots, \\
a &= 1+q\alpha(\sigma)+q^2\beta(\sigma)+q^3\gamma(\sigma)+\cdots.
\end{aligned}\right\} \tag{3.7}$$

Substituting these and (3.6) into (3.1), and equating coefficients of the same powers of q to zero, we ultimately find

$$\left.\begin{aligned}
a_3 &= 3q^2\sin 2\sigma+3q^3\sin 4\sigma+\cdots, \\
b_3 &= q+q^2\cos 2\sigma+q^3\left(-\frac{14}{3}+5\cos 4\sigma\right)+\cdots, \\
a_5 &= \frac{14}{9}q^3\sin 2\sigma+\cdots, \\
b_5 &= \frac{1}{3}q^2+\frac{4}{9}q^3\cos 2\sigma+\cdots, \\
&\cdots\cdots\cdots\cdots\cdots\cdots,
\end{aligned}\right\} \tag{3.8}$$

$$\left.\begin{aligned}
\mu &= 4q\sin 2\sigma-12q^3\sin 2\sigma+\cdots, \\
a &= 1+8q\cos 2\sigma+q^2(-16+8\cos 4\sigma)-8q^3\cos 2\sigma+\cdots.
\end{aligned}\right\} \tag{3.9}$$

As far as the stability is considered, it will suffice to evaluate the characteristic exponent μ only. To this end, we calculate σ by the second equation of (3.9), and then substituting this into the first, we get the value of μ.

Proceeding likewise for the unstable solution associated with the second unstable region interposed between a_{c2} and a_{s2} [37], we obtain

$$\left.\begin{aligned}
\phi(\tau) &= \sin(2\tau-\sigma)+q\left[2\sin\sigma+\frac{2}{3}\sin(4\tau-\sigma)\right]+\frac{1}{6}q^2\sin(6\tau-\sigma) \\
&\quad+q^3\left[\frac{8}{3}\sin\sigma-16\sin^3\sigma-\frac{16}{9}\sin 2\sigma\cdot\cos(4\tau-\sigma)\right. \\
&\quad\left.+\left(-\frac{5}{27}+\frac{16}{9}\sin^2\sigma\right)\sin(4\tau-\sigma)+\frac{1}{45}\sin(8\tau-\sigma)\right]+\cdots,
\end{aligned}\right\} \tag{3.10}$$

$$\left.\begin{aligned}
\mu &= -4q^2\sin 2\sigma+\cdots, \\
a &= 4-q^2\left(\frac{16}{3}-32\sin^2\sigma\right)+\cdots,
\end{aligned}\right\} \tag{3.11}$$

and for the third unstable region interposed between a_{c3} and a_{s3}, we obtain

$$\phi(\tau) = \sin(3\tau - \sigma) + q\left[-\sin(\tau - \sigma) + \frac{1}{2}\sin(5\tau - \sigma)\right]$$
$$+ q^2\left[-\sin(\tau + \sigma) + \frac{1}{10}\sin(7\tau - \sigma)\right]$$
$$+ q^3\left[-\frac{1}{2}\sin(\tau - \sigma) + \frac{7}{40}\sin(5\tau - \sigma) + \frac{1}{90}\sin(9\tau - \sigma)\right] + \cdots,$$

(3.12)

$$\mu = \frac{4}{3}q^3\sin 2\sigma + \cdots,$$
$$a = 9 + 4q^2 + 8q^3\cos 2\sigma + \cdots.$$

(3.13)

From the foregoing analysis the characteristic exponent μ is readily calculated when the new parameter σ is known. Practically, however, when Mathieu's equation is to be solved, the parameters a and q are first known, and it is rather difficult to find σ from given values of a and q. To avoid this situation, a and μ are first calculated from equations (3.9), (3.11), and (3.13) by varying q and σ, and then the iso-μ and iso-σ curves are plotted in the a, q-plane as illustrated in Figs. 3.2 to 3.4. These figures correspond respectively to the first, the second, and the third unstable regions which are shown shaded in Fig. 3.1. Thus, μ and σ are directly evaluated when a and q are given.

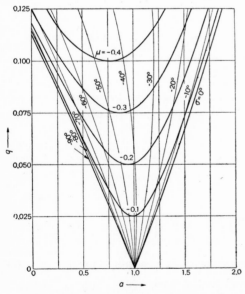

FIG. 3.2. Iso-μ and iso-σ curves in the first unstable region.

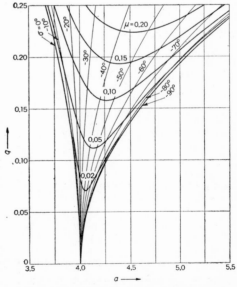

FIG. 3.3. Iso-μ and iso-σ curves in the second unstable region.

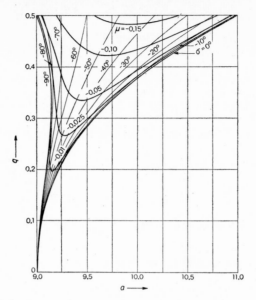

Fıɢ. 3. 4. Iso-μ and iso-σ curves in the third unstable region

4. 1. Stability problem for Hill's equation

Hill's equation [13, 45, 52, 53] takes the form

$$\frac{d^2x}{d\tau^2} + \left(\theta_0 + 2\sum_{\nu=1}^{\infty}\theta_\nu\cos 2\nu\tau\right)x = 0\,, \tag{4.1}$$

where θ_0, θ_1, θ_2, $\cdots$ are assigned parameters and $\sum_{\nu=1}^{\infty}|\theta_\nu|$ converges. The theory in the preceding sections applies (*mutatis mutandis*) to Hill's equation, and so the solution of (4.1) may be either stable or unstable.

We shall now briefly discuss the unstable solution by making use of Whittaker's method of change of parameter. By Floquet's theory, a particular solution of (4.1) is given by

$$x = e^{\mu\tau}\phi(\tau)\,. \tag{4.2}$$

Substitution of (4.2) into (4.1) gives

$$\frac{d^2\phi}{d\tau^2} + 2\mu\frac{d\phi}{d\tau} + \left[\theta_0 + \mu^2 + 2\sum_{\nu=1}^{\infty}\theta_\nu\cos 2\nu\tau\right]\phi = 0\,. \tag{4.3}$$

Following Whittaker, the periodic function $\phi(\tau)$ in the nth unstable region may be assumed (to a first approximation) in the form

$$\phi(\tau) = \sin(n\tau - \sigma)\,, \qquad n = 1, 2, 3, \cdots, \tag{4.4}$$

in which σ is a new parameter to be determined presently. Substituting (4.4) into (4.3) and equating the coefficients of $\sin n\tau$ and $\cos n\tau$ separately to zero, we obtain

$$\left.\begin{aligned}
2\mu n \sin \sigma + (\theta_0 + \mu^2 - n^2) \cos \sigma - \theta_n \cos \sigma = 0, \\
2\mu n \cos \sigma - (\theta_0 + \mu^2 - n^2) \sin \sigma - \theta_n \sin \sigma = 0.
\end{aligned}\right\} \tag{4.5}$$

Hence the characteristic exponent μ and the parameter σ are given by

$$\left.\begin{aligned}
\mu &= \frac{\theta_n}{2n} \sin 2\sigma, \\
\\
\theta_0 &= n^2 + \theta_n \cos 2\sigma - \left(\frac{\theta_n}{2n}\right)^2 \sin^2 2\sigma,
\end{aligned}\right\} \tag{4.6}$$

with

from which, upon eliminating σ, we obtain

$$\mu^2 = -(\theta_0 + n^2) \pm \sqrt{4n^2\theta_0 + \theta_n^2}. \tag{4.7}$$

From equations (4.6), μ and σ are obtained for given θ_0 and θ_n, so that the particular solution (4.2) with (4.4) is readily determined. Furthermore, if we write $-\sigma$ for σ in (4.6), the value of θ_0 is unchanged, but this change alters the sign of μ. Hence we see that the second independent solution may take the form

$$x = e^{-\mu\tau} \sin(n\tau + \sigma),$$

and the complete solution, with two arbitrary constants, is

$$x = c_1 e^{\mu\tau} \sin(n\tau - \sigma) + c_2 e^{-\mu\tau} \sin(n\tau + \sigma). \tag{4.8}$$

Since the characteristic exponent μ may be taken to be purely imaginary or real according as whether the solution is stable or unstable, we have $\mu^2 > 0$ for the unstable solution. This condition is transformed by (4.7) to

$$\left.\begin{aligned}
(\theta_0 - n^2 + \theta_n)(\theta_0 - n^2 - \theta_n) < 0, \\
\\
|\theta_n| > |\theta_0 - n^2|.
\end{aligned}\right\} \tag{4.9}$$

or

Since $\mu = 0$ on the boundary between the stable and unstable regions, the boundary lines of the nth unstable region are given by

$$\theta_0 = n^2 \pm \theta_n, \tag{4.10}$$

which are also derived directly by putting $\sigma = -\pi/2$ and $\sigma = 0$ in the second equation of (4.6).

It is apparent from these equations that the values of μ, σ and consequently the boundary of the nth unstable region are determined only by θ_0 and θ_n, and are not affected by other parameters. This is because we have confined our calculation to a first approximation. By closer approximation, however, the remaining parameters are related to it, as will be shown in Appendix II where the parameters are taken into account up to the third power.*

4.2. Extended form of Hill's equation

Thus far we have considered Mathieu's and Hill's equations as the representative cases of equation (2.6) in Section 2. More generally, however, the form of equation (2.6) may be represented by

$$\frac{d^2x}{d\tau^2}+\left[\theta_0+2\sum_{\nu=1}^{\infty}\theta_{\nu s}\sin 2\nu\tau+2\sum_{\nu=1}^{\infty}\theta_{\nu c}\cos 2\nu\tau\right]x=0, \qquad (4.11)$$

which may be considered as an extended form of Hill's equation. Whittaker's method of solution may likewise be applied in this case, and assuming for x the following first approximation

$$x=e^{\mu\tau}\sin(n\tau-\sigma), \qquad n=1,\,2,\,3,\,\cdots, \qquad (4.12)$$

we obtain

$$\left.\begin{array}{l} 2\mu n=\theta_{nc}\sin 2\sigma-\theta_{ns}\cos 2\sigma, \\[4pt] \theta_0=n^2-\mu^2+\theta_{ns}\sin 2\sigma+\theta_{nc}\cos 2\sigma. \end{array}\right\} \qquad (4.13)$$

Elimination of σ in (4.13) leads to

$$\mu^2=-(\theta_0+n^2)\pm\sqrt{4n^2\theta_0+\theta_n^2}, \qquad \theta_n^2=\theta_{ns}^2+\theta_{nc}^2. \qquad (4.14)$$

This is identical with equation (4.7), but we have two different values of σ (in magnitude) from (4.13), and denoting them by σ_1 and σ_2 respectively, we get the general solution

$$x=c_1e^{\mu\tau}\sin(n\tau-\sigma_1)+c_2e^{-\mu\tau}\sin(n\tau-\sigma_2). \qquad (4.15)$$

The above consideration is confined to the first approximation. In Appendix III the closer approximation is carried out in which the terms are taken into account up to the second degree of the θ's.

---

* See also Reference [15].

4.3. Improved first approximation in the unstable regions of even orders (*n* even)

In the preceding two sections we have assumed the first approximation of the unstable solution to take the form

$$x = e^{\mu\tau}\phi(\tau) = e^{\mu\tau}\sin(n\tau - \sigma).$$

But, the solution in the unstable region of even order contains constant terms[†] (see Appendix III), and so, it may be preferable to add a constant term to $\phi(\tau)$, and thus we write

$$x = e^{\mu\tau}\phi(\tau) = e^{\mu\tau}[c + \sin(n\tau - \sigma)], \qquad n = 2, 4, 6, \cdots. \qquad (4.16)$$

Substituting this into (4.11) and equating the constant term and the coefficients of $\sin n\tau$ and $\cos n\tau$ separately to zero, we obtain

$$\left. \begin{array}{l} c(\theta_0 + \mu^2) - \theta_{\frac{n}{2}c}\sin\sigma + \theta_{\frac{n}{2}s}\cos\sigma = 0, \\[2mm] 2c\theta_{\frac{n}{2}s} - (\theta_{ns} - 2n\mu)\sin\sigma + (\theta_0 + \mu^2 - n^2 - \theta_{nc})\cos\sigma = 0, \\[2mm] 2c\theta_{\frac{n}{2}c} - (\theta_0 + \mu^2 - n^2 + \theta_{nc})\sin\sigma + (\theta_{ns} + 2n\mu)\cos\sigma = 0. \end{array} \right\} \qquad (4.17)$$

Hence, eliminating c and σ in (4.17), we have

$$\begin{vmatrix} \theta_0 + \mu^2 & \theta_{\frac{n}{2}s} & \theta_{\frac{n}{2}c} \\[3mm] 2\theta_{\frac{n}{2}s} & \theta_0 + \mu^2 - n^2 - \theta_{nc} & \theta_{ns} - 2n\mu \\[3mm] 2\theta_{\frac{n}{2}c} & \theta_{ns} + 2n\mu & \theta_0 + \mu^2 - n^2 + \theta_{nc} \end{vmatrix} = 0. \qquad (4.18)$$

As mentioned in Section 4.1, the characteristic exponent μ tends to zero at the boundary between the stable and the unstable regions, and the condition $\mu^2 > 0$ holds for the unstable regions. Hence, in so far as we are concerned with the neighborhood of the boundary mentioned above, μ^2 is so small that we may neglect it as compared with θ_0 in computing the condition $\mu^2 > 0$. Thus, from (4.18), we obtain

$$\left. \begin{array}{l} 4n^2\mu^2 = -(\theta_0 - n^2)^2 + \theta_n^2 + 2\dfrac{\theta_0 - n^2}{\theta_0}\theta_{\frac{n}{2}}^2 \\[4mm] \qquad - \dfrac{2}{\theta_0}\Big[\theta_{nc}(\theta_{\frac{n}{2}c}^2 - \theta_{\frac{n}{2}s}^2) + 2\theta_{ns}\theta_{\frac{n}{2}c}\theta_{\frac{n}{2}s}\Big] > 0, \end{array} \right\} \qquad (4.19)$$

[†] It will be remembered that the Mathieu function $ce_2(\tau, q)$ contains constant terms [see equations (3.4) and Appendix I].

or

$$\begin{vmatrix} \theta_0 & \theta_{\frac{n}{2}s} & \theta_{\frac{n}{2}c} \\[2mm] 2\theta_{\frac{n}{2}s} & \theta_0 - n^2 - \theta_{nc} & \theta_{ns} \\[2mm] 2\theta_{\frac{n}{2}c} & \theta_{ns} & \theta_0 - n^2 + \theta_{nc} \end{vmatrix} < 0. \qquad (4.20)$$

These are the conditions for equation (4.11) to have an unstable solution in the nth (even) region.

5.1.   Condition for the stability of non-linear periodic oscillations [11]

Following the preceding considerations, we shall derive the stability condition for the periodic oscillations governed by the following equation:

$$\frac{d^2v}{d\tau^2} + 2\delta\frac{dv}{d\tau} + f(v) = e(\tau), \qquad (5.1)$$

in which 2δ is a constant damping coefficient, $f(v)$ a non-linear term, and $e(\tau)$ a periodic external force. Let the variation of v be ξ; then corresponding to equations (2.5) and (2.6), we have

$$\xi = e^{-\delta\tau}\cdot\eta, \qquad (5.2)$$

and

$$\frac{d^2\eta}{d\tau^2} + \left(\frac{df}{dv} - \delta^2\right)\eta = 0. \qquad (5.3)$$

Now, once the periodic state of equilibrium is determined (usually by applying either iteration or perturbation method), the coefficient of η in (5.3) may be developed into a Fourier series, and we consider the following two cases.

(1)   When the series contains only even harmonics, equation (5.3) becomes

$$\frac{d^2\eta}{d\tau^2} + \left[\theta_0 + 2\sum_{\nu=1}^{\infty}\theta_\nu\cos\left(2\nu\tau - \varepsilon_\nu\right)\right]\eta = 0. \qquad (5.4)$$

According to the investigation in Section 2, the stability condition in this case is given by $\delta > |\mu|$, or, substituting (4.14), we obtain

$$(\theta_0 - n^2)^2 + 2(\theta_0 + n^2)\delta^2 + \delta^4 > \theta_n^2, \qquad n = 1, 2, 3, \cdots. \qquad (5.5)$$

This is the stability condition (of the first approximation*) for the nth unstable

---

* In the case when the stability condition of a higher order approximation is required, we should refer to Appendices II and III for the closer evaluation of μ.

region, so that, in order for a periodic state of equilibrium to be stable, the condition (5.5) must be satisfied for all values of n simultaneously.

(2) When the series contains even and odd harmonics, equation (5.3) leads to

$$\frac{d^2\eta}{d\tau^2} + \left[\theta_0 + 2\sum_{\nu=1}^{\infty}\theta_\nu\cos(\nu\tau - \varepsilon_\nu)\right]\eta = 0. \tag{5.6}$$

The stability condition may be derived in the same manner as in the preceding case, and it becomes

$$\left[\theta_0 - \left(\frac{n}{2}\right)^2\right]^2 + 2\left[\theta_0 + \left(\frac{n}{2}\right)^2\right]\delta^2 + \delta^4 > \theta_n^2, \qquad n = 1, 2, 3, \cdots. \tag{5.7}$$

5.2. Improved stability condition for n even

Following the consideration in Section 4.3, we shall derive the improved first approximation of the stability condition for the unstable regions of even orders.

(a) When the variational equation leads to (5.4), η will take the form

$$\eta = e^{\mu\tau}[c + \sin(n\tau - \sigma)], \qquad n = 2, 4, 6, \cdots. \tag{5.8}$$

Hence the characteristic exponent μ is determined by equation (4.18), or

$$\begin{vmatrix} \theta_0 + \delta^2 + \mu^2 - \delta^2 & \theta_{\frac{n}{2}s} & \theta_{\frac{n}{2}c} \\ 2\theta_{\frac{n}{2}s} & \theta_0 + \delta^2 + \mu^2 - \delta^2 - n^2 - \theta_{nc} & \theta_{ns} - 2n\mu \\ 2\theta_{\frac{n}{2}c} & \theta_{ns} + 2n\mu & \theta_0 + \delta^2 + \mu^2 - \delta^2 - n^2 + \theta_{nc} \end{vmatrix} = 0. \tag{5.9}$$

The stability condition is given by $\delta^2 - \mu^2 > 0$, and we may neglect $\mu^2 - \delta^2$ as compared with $\theta_0 + \delta^2$ in computing this condition (in the same manner as we have done in Section 4.3). Therefore we have

$$\left.\begin{aligned} 4n^2(\delta^2 - \mu^2) &= (\theta_0 + \delta^2 - n^2)^2 - \theta_n^2 - 2\frac{\theta_0 + \delta^2 - n^2}{\theta_0 + \delta^2}\theta_{\frac{n}{2}}^2 \\ &\quad + \frac{2}{\theta_0 + \delta^2}\left[\theta_{nc}(\theta_{\frac{n}{2}c}^2 - \theta_{\frac{n}{2}s}^2) + 2\theta_{ns}\theta_{\frac{n}{2}c}\theta_{\frac{n}{2}s}\right] + 4n^2\delta^2 > 0, \end{aligned}\right\} \tag{5.10}$$

or

$$\begin{vmatrix} \theta_0 + \delta^2 & \theta_{\frac{n}{2}s} & \theta_{\frac{n}{2}c} \\ 2\theta_{\frac{n}{2}s} & \theta_0 + \delta^2 - n^2 - \theta_{nc} & \theta_{ns} - 2n\delta \\ 2\theta_{\frac{n}{2}c} & \theta_{ns} + 2n\delta & \theta_0 + \delta^2 - n^2 + \theta_{nc} \end{vmatrix} > 0. \tag{5.11}$$

These are the improved stability conditions for the nth (even) unstable region.

(b) When the variational equation leads to (5.6), η will take the form

$$\eta = e^{\mu\tau} \left[c + \sin\left(\frac{n}{2}\tau - \sigma \right) \right], \qquad n = 2,\ 4,\ 6,\cdots . \tag{5.12}$$

Proceeding in the same manner as in Sections 4.3 and 5.2 (a), the improved stability condition may be derived for the nth (even) unstable region as follows:

$$\left. \begin{aligned} n^2(\delta^2 - \mu^2) &= \left[\theta_0 + \delta^2 - \left(\frac{n}{2}\right)^2 \right]^2 - \theta_n^2 - 2\,\frac{\theta_0 + \delta^2 - \left(\frac{n}{2}\right)^2}{\theta_0 + \delta^2}\,\theta_{\frac{n}{2}}^2 \\ &\quad + \frac{2}{\theta_0 + \delta^2}\left[\theta_{nc}\left(\theta_{\frac{n}{2}c}^2 - \theta_{\frac{n}{2}s}^2\right) + 2\theta_{ns}\theta_{\frac{n}{2}c}\theta_{\frac{n}{2}s} \right] + n^2\delta^2 > 0, \end{aligned} \right\} \tag{5.13}$$

or

$$\begin{vmatrix} \theta_0 + \delta^2 & \theta_{\frac{n}{2}s} & \theta_{\frac{n}{2}c} \\[2ex] 2\theta_{\frac{n}{2}s} & \theta_0 + \delta^2 - \left(\frac{n}{2}\right)^2 - \theta_{nc} & \theta_{ns} - n\delta \\[2ex] 2\theta_{\frac{n}{2}c} & \theta_{ns} + n\delta & \theta_0 + \delta^2 - \left(\frac{n}{2}\right)^2 + \theta_{nc} \end{vmatrix} > 0. \tag{5.14}$$

5.3. Complementary remarks on the stability conditions

(a) Stability condition (5.5) for $n = 1$

We shall first consider the condition (5.5) for the first unstable region. Since the solution of equation (5.3) is, in this case, of the form $e^{\mu\tau}$ [$\sin(\tau - \sigma)$ $+$ higher oder terms in $\theta_1,\ \theta_2,\cdots$], the condition (5.5) ascertains the stability against building up of the unstable oscillation in which the component having the fundamental frequency predominates over the higher harmonics.

Now, in order to discuss the stability condition concretely, let us take an example

$$\frac{d^2v}{d\tau^2} + 2\delta\frac{dv}{d\tau} + f(v) = B\cos\tau, \tag{5.15}$$

where $f(v)$ is odd in v, and consider the case in which a periodic solution is approximated by

$$v = x\sin\tau + y\cos\tau. \tag{5.16}$$

The amplitudes x and y may readily be found as follows. Namely, substituting (5.16) into (5.15) and equating the coefficients of $\sin\tau$ and $\cos\tau$ on both sides respectively, we obtain the following simultaneous equations to determine x and y, i. e.,

$$X(x,\ y) = -x - 2\delta y + \frac{1}{\pi} \int_0^{2\pi} f(v) \sin \tau d\tau = 0 \,,$$

$$Y(x,\ y) = -y + 2\delta x + \frac{1}{\pi} \int_0^{2\pi} f(v) \cos \tau d\tau = B \,. \qquad (5.17)$$

Under the present circumstances the variational equation leads to the form (5.4), and in fact we obtain,

$$\frac{d^2\eta}{d\tau^2} + \left[\theta_0 + 2 \sum_{\nu=1}^\infty \theta_{\nu s} \sin 2\nu\tau + 2 \sum_{\nu=1}^\infty \theta_{\nu c} \cos 2\nu\tau \right] \eta = 0 \,,$$

where

$$\theta_0 = \frac{1}{2\pi} \int_0^{2\pi} \frac{df}{dv} d\tau - \delta^2 \,,$$

$$\theta_{1s} = \frac{1}{2\pi} \int_0^{2\pi} \frac{df}{dv} \sin 2\tau d\tau = \frac{1}{\pi} \int_0^{2\pi} \frac{df}{dv} \cos \tau \cdot \sin \tau d\tau$$

$$= \frac{1}{\pi} \int_0^{2\pi} \frac{df}{dv} \frac{\partial v}{\partial y} \sin \tau d\tau = \frac{\partial X}{\partial y} + 2\delta$$

$$= \frac{1}{\pi} \int_0^{2\pi} \frac{df}{dv} \frac{\partial v}{\partial x} \cos \tau d\tau = \frac{\partial Y}{\partial x} - 2\delta \,,$$

$$\theta_{1c} = \frac{1}{2\pi} \int_0^{2\pi} \frac{df}{dv} \cos 2\tau d\tau = \frac{1}{\pi} \int_0^{2\pi} \frac{df}{dv} \cos^2 \tau d\tau$$

$$- \frac{1}{2\pi} \int_0^{2\pi} \frac{df}{dv} d\tau = \frac{\partial Y}{\partial y} + 1 - \theta_0 - \delta^2$$

$$= \frac{1}{2\pi} \int_0^{2\pi} \frac{df}{dv} dv - \frac{1}{\pi} \int_0^{2\pi} \frac{df}{dv} \sin^2 \tau d\tau = \theta_0 + \delta^2 - 1 - \frac{\partial X}{\partial x} \,,$$

$$\cdots\cdots\cdots\cdots\cdots \,.$$

$$(5.18)$$

Now, the stability condition (5.5) may be written in the alternative form

$$\begin{vmatrix} \theta_0 + \delta^2 - n^2 - \theta_{nc} & \theta_{ns} - 2n\delta \\ \theta_{ns} + 2n\delta & \theta_0 + \delta^2 - n^2 + \theta_{nc} \end{vmatrix} > 0 \,. \qquad (5.19)$$

Putting $n = 1$ and substituting the parameters θ_{1s} and θ_{1c} as given by (5.18), the stability condition (5.5) finally leads to

$$\begin{vmatrix} \dfrac{\partial X}{\partial x} & \dfrac{\partial X}{\partial y} \\ \dfrac{\partial Y}{\partial x} & \dfrac{\partial Y}{\partial y} \end{vmatrix} > 0 \,. \qquad (5.20)$$

The last form of the stability condition is also derived from the well-known Routh-Hurwitz's criterion [14, 50]. To verify this, let the variations of the amplitudes x and y be $\xi(\tau)$ and $\eta(\tau)$ respectively, and write

$$v(\tau) = x(\tau)\sin\tau + y(\tau)\cos\tau,$$

with

$$x(\tau) = x + \xi(\tau), \quad y(\tau) = y + \eta(\tau). \qquad (5.21)$$

Then, if $\xi(\tau)$ and $\eta(\tau)$ tend to zero with the lapse of time τ, the corresponding periodic solution (5.16) may be said to be stable. Substituting (5.21) into (5.15) and equating the coefficients of $\sin\tau$ and $\cos\tau$ on both sides respectively, we obtain

$$-2\frac{d\eta}{d\tau} + \frac{\partial X}{\partial x}\xi + \frac{\partial X}{\partial y}\eta = 0,$$

$$2\frac{d\xi}{d\tau} + \frac{\partial Y}{\partial x}\xi + \frac{\partial Y}{\partial y}\eta = 0, \qquad (5.22)$$

where, for the simplicity of analysis, it is assumed that the damping coefficient δ is very small and also that $\xi(\tau)$ and $\eta(\tau)$ are so slowly variable (with time) that $d^2\xi/d\tau^2$ and $d^2\eta/d\tau^2$ may be neglected. The solutions of these simultaneous equations have the form $e^{\lambda\tau}$, where λ is determined by the characteristic equation

$$\begin{vmatrix} \dfrac{\partial X}{\partial x} & \dfrac{\partial X}{\partial y} - 2\lambda \\[2mm] \dfrac{\partial Y}{\partial x} + 2\lambda & \dfrac{\partial Y}{\partial y} \end{vmatrix} = 0. \qquad (5.23)$$

Hence the periodic solution (5.16) is stable provided that the real part of λ is negative. This stability condition is given by Hurwitz's criterion [14] as

$$\frac{\partial Y}{\partial x} - \frac{\partial X}{\partial y} > 0,$$

$$\frac{\partial X}{\partial x}\frac{\partial Y}{\partial y} - \frac{\partial X}{\partial y}\frac{\partial Y}{\partial x} > 0. \qquad (5.24)$$

The first condition is always fulfilled, because it is transformed to $\delta > 0$ by virtue of (5.18). The second condition is the one we have already derived in (5.20).

We shall further verify that the characteristic curve (which shows the amplitude of oscillation against B) has a vertical tangent at the stability limit of the first unstable region.

To prove this, put $r^2 = x^2 + y^2$. Then the characteristic curve, i.e., the

B, r-relation, is readily obtained by solving (5.17). While, differentiating (5.17) with respect to B, we have

$$\left.\begin{aligned}
\frac{\partial X}{\partial x}\frac{dx}{dB} + \frac{\partial X}{\partial y}\frac{dy}{dB} &= 0, \\[2mm]
\frac{\partial Y}{\partial x}\frac{dx}{dB} + \frac{\partial Y}{\partial y}\frac{dy}{dB} &= 1.
\end{aligned}\right\} \tag{5.25}$$

Solving these simultaneous equations, we obtain

$$\left.\begin{aligned}
\frac{dx}{dB} &= -\frac{\partial X}{\partial y}\Big/ \varDelta, \quad \frac{dy}{dB} = \frac{\partial X}{\partial x}\Big/ \varDelta, \\[2mm]
\text{where} \qquad \varDelta &= \frac{\partial X}{\partial x}\frac{\partial Y}{\partial y} - \frac{\partial X}{\partial y}\frac{\partial Y}{\partial x}.
\end{aligned}\right\} \tag{5.26}$$

Consequently we have

$$\frac{dr}{dB} = \frac{\partial r}{\partial x}\frac{dx}{dB} + \frac{\partial r}{\partial y}\frac{dy}{dB} = \frac{1}{r}\left(y\frac{\partial X}{\partial x} - x\frac{\partial X}{\partial y}\right)\Big/ \varDelta. \tag{5.27}$$

Hence, the vertical tangency $(dr/dB \to \infty)$ results at the stability limit of the first unstable region $(\varDelta = 0)$.

Thus far we have dealt with a particular case as specified by the periodic solution (5.16), and the more detailed investigation will be given in Sections 6 and 15. Finally it should be mentioned that the same conclusion as obtained in this paragraph may also be derived for more general cases which give rise to different types of oscillation.*

(b) Stability condition (5.5) for $n \geq 2$

We lay stress on this condition since it has not explicitly been discussed hitherto, and yet it has an important role in the investigation of the stability of non-linear periodic oscillations. Stability investigations in non-linear systems are to be found in many physical and technical journals. In Appendix IV, for example, the one reported by Mandelstam and Papalexi [21] is compared with our stability condition. The analysis reveals that their criterion corresponds to our condition for $n = 1$, and offers no information for $n \geq 2$. But, in our investigation, the generalized stability condition (5.5) for the nth unstable region will furnish the criterion to distinguish the stability for the nth harmonic of the fundamental oscillation, for the solution of the variational equation in the nth unstable region has the form $e^{\mu \tau}[\sin(n\tau - \sigma) + \text{higher order terms in } \theta_1, \theta_2, \cdots]$.

---

* See Appendix IV for the discussion of the subharmonic oscillation.

Our generalized condition is effective when we investigate the harmonic oscillation in which the higher harmonics are predominant. Such an example will be investigated in Section 8.1. Our condition is also effective when we investigate the higher harmonic oscillations (see Section 9.1) and the subharmonic oscillations (see Sections 12.2 and 13.1). For example, in studying the subharmonic oscillation of order 1/3, we are frequently encountered with the self-excitation of the second harmonic of the subharmonic oscillation, i.e., the oscillation of order 2/3, which will no longer permit the continuation of the original subharmonic oscillation. Thus, the stability condition for the first unstable region is not sufficient in this case, and the instability mentioned above may be detected by putting $n = 2$ in (5.5).

(c) Stability condition (5.7)

The foregoing discussions in (a) and (b) apply as well if we write $n/2$ instead of n. Since the solution of equation (5.6) has the form $e^{\mu\tau}[\sin(n\tau/2-\sigma) +\cdots]$ in the nth unstable region, the $n/2$th harmonic of the fundamental oscillation will be excited in this region.

Thus, if we consider the differential equation (5.15), the stability condition (5.7) for $n = 1$ ascertains the stability against building up of the unstable oscillation having the frequency one-half that of the external force, and the relationships obtained in (a) will be derived by putting $n = 2$. However, the variational equation leads to the form (5.6) in the case when the non-linear function $f(v)$ in (5.15) is not odd in v, or when the external force contains a unidirectional component. In such cases the periodic solution usually contains a constant term, and consequently it will be preferable to resort to the improved stability condition investigated in Section 5.2.

(d) Improved stability condition (5.13) for $n = 2$

We shall particularly deal with this condition in detail, because it is useful in investigating the non-linear oscillations with unsymmetrical characteristic (see Sections 7.1 and 13.1).

Proceeding in the same manner as in (a) we consider a differential equation

$$\frac{d^2v}{d\tau^2} + 2\delta\frac{dv}{d\tau} + f(v) = B_0 + B\cos\tau, \qquad (5.28)$$

where the unsymmetry is given in $f(v)$ or by the presence of B_0. Now, assuming the periodic solution

$$v = v_0 + x\sin\tau + y\cos\tau, \qquad (5.29)$$

we obtain the following relations to determine v_0, x, and y, namely,

$$V_0(v_0, x, y) = \frac{1}{2\pi} \int_0^{2\pi} f(v)\, d\tau = B_0,$$

$$X(v_0, x, y) = -x - 2\delta y + \frac{1}{\pi} \int_0^{2\pi} f(v) \sin \tau d\tau = 0,$$

$$Y(v_0, x, y) = -y + 2\delta x + \frac{1}{\pi} \int_0^{2\pi} f(v) \cos \tau d\tau = B. \qquad \left.\begin{array}{c} \\ \\ \\ \end{array}\right\} (5.30)$$

Under such circumstances the variational equation leads to the form (5.6), and in fact we obtain

$$\frac{d^2\eta}{d\tau^2} + \left[\theta_0 + 2\sum_{\nu=1}^{\infty} \theta_{\nu s} \sin \nu\tau + 2\sum_{\nu=1}^{\infty} \theta_{\nu c} \cos \nu\tau \right] \eta = 0,$$

where

$$\theta_0 = \frac{1}{2\pi} \int_0^{2\pi} \frac{df}{dv}\, d\tau - \delta^2 = \frac{\partial V_0}{\partial v_0} - \delta^2,$$

$$\theta_{1s} = \frac{1}{2\pi} \int_0^{2\pi} \frac{df}{dv} \sin \tau d\tau = \frac{1}{2} \frac{\partial X}{\partial v_0} = \frac{\partial V_0}{\partial x},$$

$$\theta_{1c} = \frac{1}{2\pi} \int_0^{2\pi} \frac{df}{dv} \cos \tau d\tau = \frac{1}{2} \frac{\partial Y}{\partial v_0} = \frac{\partial V_0}{\partial y},$$

$$\theta_{2s} = \frac{1}{2\pi} \int_0^{2\pi} \frac{df}{dv} \sin 2\tau d\tau = \frac{\partial X}{\partial y} + 2\delta = \frac{\partial Y}{\partial x} - 2\delta,$$

$$\theta_{2c} = \frac{1}{2\pi} \int_0^{2\pi} \frac{df}{dv} \cos 2\tau d\tau = \frac{\partial Y}{\partial y} + 1 - \theta_0 - \delta^2 = -\frac{\partial X}{\partial x} - 1 + \theta_0 + \delta^2,$$

$$\left.\begin{array}{c} \\ \\ \\ \\ \\ \end{array}\right\} (5.31)$$

. . . .

By virtue of these relations, the stability condition (5.13) for $n = 2$ leads to

$$\Delta \equiv \begin{vmatrix} \dfrac{\partial V_0}{\partial v_0} & \dfrac{\partial V_0}{\partial x} & \dfrac{\partial V_0}{\partial y} \\[2ex] \dfrac{\partial X}{\partial v_0} & \dfrac{\partial X}{\partial x} & \dfrac{\partial X}{\partial y} \\[2ex] \dfrac{\partial Y}{\partial v_0} & \dfrac{\partial Y}{\partial x} & \dfrac{\partial Y}{\partial y} \end{vmatrix} > 0. \qquad (5.32)$$

This form of stability condition may also be derived from the Routh-Hirwitz's criterion in the same manner as we have done in the preceding paragraph (a).

Finally, we shall discuss the vertical tangency of the characteristic curve.

Putting $r^2 = x^2 + y^2$, the relationship between B, B_0 and r is readily obtained by solving (5.30).

Differentiating (5.30) with respect to B while holding B_0 constant,

$$\left.\begin{aligned}
\frac{\partial V_0}{\partial v_0}\frac{dv_0}{dB} + \frac{\partial V_0}{\partial x}\frac{dx}{dB} + \frac{\partial V_0}{\partial y}\frac{dy}{dB} &= 0, \\[1.5ex]
\frac{\partial X}{\partial v_0}\frac{dv_0}{dB} + \frac{\partial X}{\partial x}\frac{dx}{dB} + \frac{\partial X}{\partial y}\frac{dy}{dB} &= 0, \\[1.5ex]
\frac{\partial Y}{\partial v_0}\frac{dv_0}{dB} + \frac{\partial Y}{\partial x}\frac{dx}{dB} + \frac{\partial Y}{\partial y}\frac{dy}{dB} &= 1.
\end{aligned}\right\} \quad (5.33)$$

Solving these simultaneous equations, we have

$$\left.\begin{aligned}
\frac{dx}{dB} &= -\frac{\dfrac{\partial V_0}{\partial v_0}\dfrac{\partial X}{\partial y} - \dfrac{\partial V_0}{\partial y}\dfrac{\partial X}{\partial v_0}}{\varDelta}, \\[2ex]
\frac{dy}{dB} &= \frac{\dfrac{\partial V_0}{\partial v_0}\dfrac{\partial X}{\partial x} - \dfrac{\partial V_0}{\partial x}\dfrac{\partial X}{\partial v_0}}{\varDelta},
\end{aligned}\right\} \quad (5.34)$$

and consequently,

$$\left.\begin{aligned}
\frac{dr}{dB} &= \frac{\partial r}{\partial x}\frac{dx}{dB} + \frac{\partial r}{\partial y}\frac{dy}{dB} = \frac{x}{r}\frac{dx}{dB} + \frac{y}{r}\frac{dy}{dB} \\[2ex]
&= \frac{1}{r\cdot\varDelta}\left[y\left(\frac{\partial V_0}{\partial v_0}\frac{\partial X}{\partial x} - \frac{\partial V_0}{\partial x}\frac{\partial X}{\partial v_0}\right) - x\left(\frac{\partial V_0}{\partial v_0}\frac{\partial X}{\partial y} - \frac{\partial V_0}{\partial y}\frac{\partial X}{\partial v_0}\right)\right].
\end{aligned}\right\} \quad (5.35)$$

Hence the characteristic curve (B, r-relation) has a vertical tangent at the stability limit of the second unstable region.*

---

* Similar conclusion may be obtained in the case when B is constant and B_0 varies.

CHAPTER II

HARMONIC OSCILLATIONS

6. Harmonic oscillation with symmetrical non-linear characteristic

In the present chapter we shall deal with the harmonic oscillations in which the fundamental component having the same period as that of the external force is so predominant that the higher harmonics may be neglected. In order to get the physical idea concretely, we shall consider an electrical oscillatory circuit and derive the non-linear differential equation of the form (5.1) in Chapter I [7, 9, 10, 31].

(a) Fundamental equation

The schematic diagram illustrated in Fig. 6.1 shows an electrical circuit in which the non-linear oscillation takes place due to the saturable-core inductance L under the impression of the alternating electromotive force $E \sin \omega t$. As seen in the figure, the resistance R is shunted to the capacitance C to render the circuit dissipative. With the notations of Fig. 6.1, we have

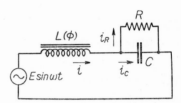

FIG. 6.1.   Oscillatory circuit with non-linear inductance.

$$\left. \begin{array}{c} n\dfrac{d\phi}{dt} + Ri_R = E \sin \omega t\,, \\[2mm] Ri_R = \dfrac{1}{C}\displaystyle\int i_C dt\,, \\[2mm] i = i_R + i_C\,, \end{array} \right\} \tag{6.1}$$

where n is the number of turns of the coil and ϕ the magnetic flux in the core.

Let us now introduce the non-dimensional variables u and v in place of i and ϕ with the relations

$$i = I_n \cdot u\,, \quad \phi = \mathit{\Phi}_n \cdot v\,, \tag{6.2}$$

where I_n and $\mathit{\Phi}_n$ are appropriate unit quantities of the current and the flux respectively. Then, neglecting hysteresis, we may assume the saturation curve of the form

$$u = c_1 v + c_3 v^3 + c_5 v^5 + \cdots\,, \tag{6.3}$$

23

where c_1, c_3, c_5, ... are constants characteristic of the core.

Although the units I_n and $\varPhi_n$ can be chosen quite arbitrarily, it is preferable, for the brevity of calculation, to fix them with the following relations:

$$\left.\begin{aligned} n\omega^2 C \varPhi_n &= I_n , \\ c_1 + c_3 + c_5 + \cdots &= 1 . \end{aligned}\right\} \tag{6.4}$$

Then, eliminating i_R and i_C in equations (6.1), and substituting (6.2), (6.3), and (6.4), we obtain

where

$$\left.\begin{aligned} \frac{d^2 v}{d\tau^2} + k\frac{dv}{d\tau} + c_1 v + c_3 v^3 + c_5 v^5 + \cdots &= B\cos\tau , \\[2mm] \tau = \omega t - \arctan k , \qquad k &= \frac{1}{\omega C R} , \\[2mm] B = \frac{E}{n\omega \varPhi_n}\sqrt{1+k^2} . \end{aligned}\right\} \tag{6.5}$$

This takes the form of equation (5.1) in which the non-linear function $f(v)$ is symmetrical, i.e., an odd function of v. A similar equation may also be obtained for the mechanical system in which the restoring force is non-linear [39, p. 78].

(b) Periodic states of equilibrium

In order to facilitate the calculation we consider the following simple but exemplary case in equation (6.3); i.e.,

$$c_5 = c_7 = \cdots = 0 , \tag{6.6}$$

so that

$$u = c_1 v + c_3 v^3 .*$$

For the harmonic oscillation in which the component of fundamental frequency predominates over the higher harmonics, the periodic solution of (6.5) takes the form†

$$v = x\sin\tau + y\cos\tau . \tag{6.7}$$

Substituting (6.7) into (6.5), and using (6.6), and further equating the terms containing $\sin\tau$ and $\cos\tau$ separately to zero, we obtain

---

* As long as we deal with the harmonic oscillation, the presence of higher powers of v (i.e., v^5, v^7, $\cdots$) causes no important change in the analysis.

† When B is large in (6.5), we have to take into account terms pertaining to higher harmonics, and this will be considered in the following chapter.

$$Ax - ky = 0 \,,$$

$$Ay + kx = B \,,$$

where

$$A = c_3\left(\frac{3}{4}r^2 - 1\right), \quad r^2 = x^2 + y^2 \,,$$

(6.8)

or, eliminating x, y in (6.8), we have

$$(A^2 + k^2)\, r^2 = B^2 \,.$$

(6.9)

This relation is rather simple, but yet shows a substantial agreement with the experimental result [7, Vol. 29, p. 601; 31, p. 728]. Figure 6.2 shows the amplitude characteristic of the harmonic oscillation, i.e., the relationship between $E/(n\omega\Phi_n)$ and r^2 for the case when $c_1 = 0.1$ and $c_3 = 0.9$.

(c) Stability condition of the periodic solutions

The periodic states of equilibrium determined by equations (6.8) or (6.9) are not always sustained, but are only able to last so long as they are stable. Following the analysis of the preceding chapter, we shall investigate the stability of the equilibrium states and find the periodic solutoins which actually exist in stable states. To effect this we consider the small variation ξ from the equilibrium states, and substituting $v + \xi$ in place of v in equation

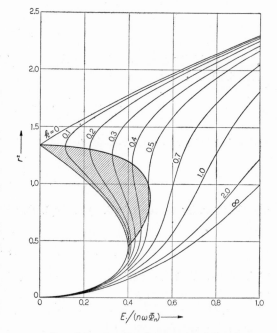

Fig. 6.2. Amplitude characteristic of the harmonic oscillation.

(6.5), and remembering the condition (6.6), we obtain the variational equation

$$\frac{d^2\xi}{d\tau^2} + k\frac{d\xi}{d\tau} + c_1\xi + 3c_3v^2\xi = 0 \,.$$

By the use of the transformation

$$\xi = e^{-\frac{1}{2}k\tau}\cdot\eta \,,$$

this leads to

$$\frac{d^2\eta}{d\tau^2} + \left(c_1 - \frac{1}{4}k^2 + 3c_3v^2\right)\eta = 0 \,.$$

Now, substituting the periodic solution (6.7), we finally obtain Mathieu's equation

$$\frac{d^2\eta}{d\tau^2} + [\theta_0 + 2\theta_1 \cos(2\tau - \varepsilon)]\eta = 0 \,,$$

where

$$\theta_0 = c_1 - \frac{1}{4}k^2 + \frac{3}{2}c_3r^2 \,,$$

$$\theta_1 = \frac{3}{4}c_3r^2 \,,$$

$$\varepsilon = \arctan \frac{2xy}{y^2 - x^2} \,.$$

(6.10)

The stability condition for the first unstable region ($n = 1$) is given by equation (5.5) in the preceding chapter, i.e.,

$$(\theta_0 - 1)^2 + \frac{1}{2}(\theta_0 + 1)k^2 + \frac{1}{16}k^4 > \theta_1^2 \,,$$

and substituting the values of θ_0 and θ_1 of (6.10), we obtain

$$c_3^2\left[\frac{27}{16}r^4 - 3r^2 + 1\right] + k^2 > 0 \,,$$

(6.11)

and further, by virtue of (6.8) and (6.9), this leads to

$$\frac{dB^2}{dr^2} > 0 \,, \quad \text{or} \quad \frac{dE^2}{dr^2} > 0 \,.$$

(6.12)

This shows that the periodic solution is stable under circumstances where the amplitude r increases with increasing external force B. From the physical point of view, this is quite a plausible condition. In Fig. 6.2 the region of unstable solution is represented by hatched lines where dB^2/dr^2 is negative. It should also be mentioned that the boundary curve between the stable and the unstable regions is determined by the condition

$$\frac{dB^2}{dr^2} = 0 \,,$$

which we could have expected from the investigation in Section 5.3 (a).

Thus we see that there are three kinds of equilibrium state under certain values of k and E. Two of these are stable and the remaining one is unstable. As mentioned in Section 5.3 (a), this unstable state is transferred to either one of the stable states owing to the building up of the unstable oscillation of the form $e^{\mu\tau}[\sin(\tau-\sigma)+\cdots]$, with $\mu>0$. In order to distinguish these two stable states, we shall call them the *resonant* and the *non-resonant* states according as the amplitude of the oscillation is large or small. Now, starting from the origin in Fig. 6.2, the amplitude r increases slowly with the increase of E (k being held constant), and so the oscillation is in the non-resonant state. When the equilibrium state gets to the boundary of the hatched region, a further increase in E will cause a jump to the resonant state with an accompanying increase in the amplitude r, after which r increases slowly with E. Upon reversing the process, i. e., with decreasing E, the oscillation jumps down from the resonant to the non-resonant state.* This transition takes place at a lower value of E than before. If we choose E between these two critical values and impress it suddenly on the circuit, either the resonant or the non-resonant oscillation results depending upon the initial condition prescribed.†

Thus far we have discussed the stability condition for $n=1$. Generally speaking, the condition for $n\geq 2$ must be considered at the same time. But, as will be discussed later in Section 8.1, this comes into question only when θ_0 is large. In such a case r^2 and B also become large, so that the higher harmonics have to be taken into account in the assumed solution of (6.7). The detailed investigation of the higher harmonic oscillation is deferred to Chapter III. It is mentioned here that the condition for $n=1$ alone will be sufficient to determine the stability in the case when B is not so large.

7.1 Harmonic oscillation with unsymmetrical non-linear characteristic

(a) Fundamental equations

When terms of v^2, $v^4, \cdots$ are present in equation (6.3), the characteristic becomes unsymmetrical, and the resulting oscillation presents some aspects different from the symmetrical case. We consider the following special case, i.e.,

$$u = c_1 v + c_2 v^2 + c_3 v^3 , \qquad (7.1)$$

whereby, equation (6.5) is modified to

$$\frac{d^2v}{d\tau^2} + k\frac{dv}{d\tau} + c_1 v + c_2 v^2 + c_3 v^3 = B \cos \tau . \qquad (7.2)$$

This equation is readily transformed to the alternative form

---

* For such an anomalous phenomenon which occurs in an electrical circuit with saturable iron-core, the term "ferro-resonance" is usually applied.

† Further investigation of this point will be discussed in Part II.

$$\frac{d^2v'}{d\tau^2}+k\frac{dv'}{d\tau}+c_1'v'+c_3'v'^3 = B\cos\tau+B_0\,,\qquad(7.3)$$

in which $v' = v+c_2/(3c_3)$, and c_1', c_3', B_0 are constants determined from c_1, c_2 and c_3. Thus we see from equation (7.3) that the non-linear characteristic is symmetrical, but the external force is unsymmetrical since it contains the unidirectional component B_0.

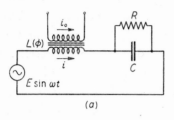

(a)

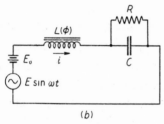

(b)

FIG. 7.1. Oscillatory circuits with unsymmetrical characteristic.

We can actually realize the electrical systems, the circuit equations of which take the forms of (7.2) and (7.3). The schematic diagrams of these systems are illustrated in Fig. 7.1a and b respectively. The saturable reactor in Fig. 7.1a has a secondary coil through which the biasing direct current flows, so that the saturation curve takes the form (7.1). In Fig. 7.1b, the d-c voltage E_0 is superimposed on the alternating voltage $E\sin\omega t$, and so equation (7.3) results.

We shall, in the end, consider the following equation for the case of the unsymmetrical characteristic; i.e.,

$$\frac{d^2v}{d\tau^2}+k\frac{dv}{d\tau}+v^3 = B\cos\tau+B_0\,,\qquad(7.4)$$

in which the linear term in v is dropped since it makes no significant change in the analysis.

(b) Periodic states of equilibrium

In the case when the system is unsymmetrical, the flux in the iron core may generally have a unidirectional component, so that we assume for v,

$$v = v_0+x\sin\tau+y\cos\tau\,.\qquad(7.5)$$

Substituting (7.5) into (7.4), and equating the constant term and the coefficients of $\sin\tau$ and $\cos\tau$ on both sides, we have

$$\left.\begin{array}{l} v_0^3+\dfrac{3}{2}v_0r^2 = B_0\,, \\[2mm] Ax-ky = 0\,, \\[2mm] Ay+kx = B\,, \end{array}\right\}\qquad(7.6)$$

where

$$A = 3v_0^2+\frac{3}{4}r^2-1\,,\quad r^2 = x^2+y^2\,,$$

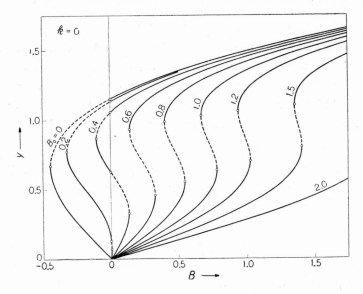

FIG. 7.2. Amplitude characteristic of the harmonic oscillation
with unsymmetrical characteristic (non-dissipative case).

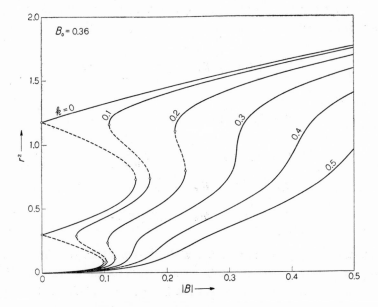

FIG. 7.3. Amplitude characteristic of the harmonic oscillation
with unsymmetrical characteristic (dissipative case).

or, eliminating x, y from the second and the third equations of (7.6),

$$(A^2+k^2)r^2 = B^2. \tag{7.7}$$

The periodic states of equilibrium will be obtained by solving (7.6). Figure 7.2 shows the amplitude y of the harmonic oscillation for the non-dissipative case, i.e., for $k = 0$ (x being zero in this case). Further, in Fig. 7.3, the relationship between $|B|$ and r^2 is illustrated for $B_0 = 0.36$. Thus we see that there are five kinds of equilibrium states under certain values of $|B|$ and k.

(c) Stability condition of the periodic solutions

We shall now determine the stability of the equilibrium states. Proceeding in the same manner as in the last section, the variation ξ from the equilibrium states will satisfy the equation

$$\frac{d^2\xi}{d\tau^2}+k\frac{d\xi}{d\tau}+3v^2\xi = 0.$$

By making use of the transformation

$$\xi = e^{-\frac{1}{2}k\tau}\cdot\eta,$$

and substituting the periodic solution (7.5), we have the variational equation of Hill's type, namely,

$$\left.\begin{aligned}
&\frac{d^2\eta}{d\tau^2}+\left[\theta_0+2\sum_{n=1}^{2}\theta_n\cos{(n\tau-\varepsilon_n)}\right]\eta = 0, \\[2mm]
&\text{where}\\[2mm]
&\theta_0 = 3v_0^2+\frac{3}{2}r^2-\frac{1}{4}k^2, \\[3mm]
&\theta_n^2 = \theta_{ns}^2+\theta_{nc}^2, \quad \varepsilon_n = \arctan\frac{\theta_{ns}}{\theta_{nc}}, \\[3mm]
&\theta_{1s} = 3v_0x, \qquad \theta_{1c} = 3v_0y, \\[3mm]
&\theta_{2s} = \frac{3}{2}xy, \qquad \theta_{2c} = \frac{3}{4}(y^2-x^2).
\end{aligned}\right\} \tag{7.8}$$

This takes the form (5.6), and so the stability condition will be given by (5.7). We shall particularly discuss the stability condition for the second unstable region in order to ascertain the stability against building up of the unstable oscillation having the same frequency as that of the periodic solution (7.5). We are, however, concerned with the unsymmetrical system and a consideration of the constant term v_0 in (7.5); therefore it will be preferable to resort to the improved stability condition (5.13) instead of (5.7). Thus we put $n = 2$ in (5.13) and write

$$4(\delta^2 - \mu^2) = (\theta_0 + \delta^2 - 1)^2 - \theta_2^2 - 2\frac{\theta_0 + \delta^2 - 1}{\theta_0 + \delta^2}\theta_1^2$$

$$+ \frac{2}{\theta_0 + \delta^2}[\theta_{2c}(\theta_{1c}^2 - \theta_{1s}^2) + 2\theta_{2s}\theta_{1c}\theta_{1s}] + 4\delta^2 > 0, \qquad (7.9)$$

where $\delta = k/2$. Substituting the parameters as given by (7.8), we obtain

$$\left(A + \frac{3}{4}r^2\right)^2 - \frac{9}{16}r^4 + k^2 - \frac{6v_0^2 r^2 A}{v_0^2 + \frac{r^2}{2}} > 0, \qquad (7.10)$$

or, by virtue of equations (7.6) and (7.7), this leads to

$$\frac{dB^2}{dr^2} > 0 .* \qquad (7.11)$$

From these stability conditions we see that the dotted-line curves in Figs. 7.2 and 7.3 represent the unstable states.

We have also to deal with the stability condition in the other unstable regions, but in so far as we are concerned with the range of B as illustrated in Figs. 7.2 and 7.3, no significant result is obtained, and therefore further discussion is omitted here.

Thus in the end we may conclude that, when the system is unsymmetrical as described by equations (7.2) or (7.4), three kinds of periodic oscillation are sustained in certain ranges of B.

7.2 Experimental investigation

In this section we shall show some experimental results in order to compare with the foregoing analysis. Generally, when a secondary winding is provided on the saturable core as illustrated in Fig. 7.1, a pulsating current would flow in it due to induction from the primary oscillating current. To suppress this a–c component in the secondary circuit, we resort to a circuit as shown in Fig. 7.4. In the figure, two reactors are used in which the secondary windings are so connected that the a–c voltages induced in them counteract each other. Further, as the degree of saturation is raised, the second harmonic current begins

---

* If we use the stability condition (5.7) instead of (5.13), the last term in the left-hand side of (7.10) is dropped and the condition (7.11) does not result.

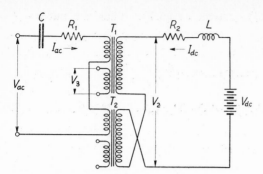

FIG. 7.4. Oscillatory circuit containing reactors with d-c superimposed.

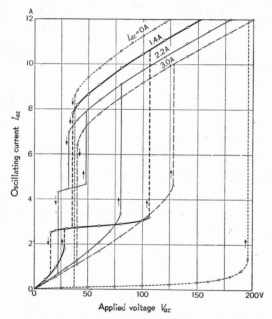

FIG. 7.5. Amplitude characteristic of the harmonic oscillation with unsymmetrical characteristic.

to flow in the d–c circuit (as will be shown in the oscillograms of Fig. 7.6); and so a coil L of high inductance is inserted to reduce this pulsation.

Now, referring to the notations in Fig. 7.4, the relationship between V_{ac} and I_{ac} is depicted in Fig. 7.5 for several values of I_{dc}. The thick-line curve in the figure is the characteristic for $I_{dc} = 1.4$ amp. In this case, as the voltage V_{ac} is increased, the oscillating current I_{ac} jumps twice with an accompanying increase in the magnitude. Upon performing the experiment in the reverse direction, i.e., with decreasing V_{ac}, it is found that the same curve is not retraced completely, but each jump from the higher to the lower current takes place at a lower value than before. Thus we see that between the resonant and the non-resonant states, there exists the third stable state which we shall hereafter call the *subresonant* state. This result agrees with the preceding analysis.

The voltage and the current wave-forms in these three states are illustrated in Fig. 7.6. Oscillogram (a) is taken for the case when the applied voltage V_{ac} is gradually raised. The two jumps of the oscillating current I_{ac} are marked by the arrows, the first one indicating the transition from the non-resonant to the subresonant state and the second from the subresonant to the resonant state. Oscillograms (b), (c), and (d) show more clearly the wave forms in these states.

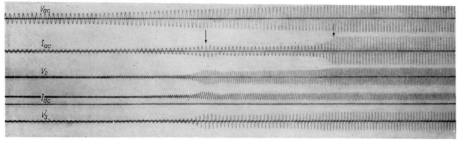

(a) Oscillation with increasing V_{ac}

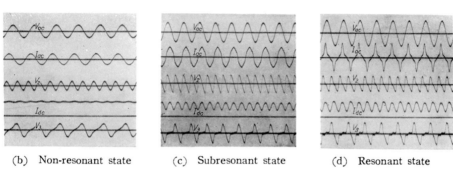

(b) Non-resonant state   (c) Subresonant state   (d) Resonant state

FIG. 7.6. Wave forms of voltages and currents in a system with
unsymmetrical characteristic.

We see that the current I_{ac} is first leading in the non-resonant state, then lagging in the subresonant state, and again leading in the resonant state, and that, as V_{ac} is increased, the second harmonic current increases predominantly in the d–c circuit.

Further, the regions in which these three states obtain are determined by experiment and depicted in Fig. 7.7. The arrows in the figure show the transition of these states when V_{ac} is changed in the direction as indicated in the figure. Thus, taking the case of $I_{dc} = 1.5$ amp.,

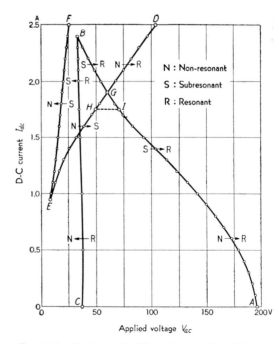

FIG. 7.7. Regions of different types of oscillation.

say, the oscillation is transferred from the non-resonant to the subresonant state when V_{ac} is raised up to the boundary DE, and further is transferred from the subresonant to the resonant state when V_{ac} crosses over the boundary AB. It should be mentioned that when V_{ac} is increased and made to cross over the portion GH of the boundary DE, the oscillation jumps directly from the non-resonant to the resonant state. The boundary GI may be determined by holding V_{ac} constant and gradually increasing I_{dc} from a lower value for which the oscillation is in the subresonant state. We see in the end that the subresonant state is able to take place provided that the direct current I_{dc} is chosen at a value between B and E.

CHAPTER III

HIGHER HARMONIC OSCILLATIONS

8.1. Higher harmonic oscillations in series-oscillation circuits

Very few investigations have been reported done in this field; however, it should be noticed that oscillations of this kind are worthy of consideration since anomalous phenomena may take place under certain circumstances [7, Vol. 29, p. 670; 31, p. 778]. Referring to the electrical circuit of Fig. 6.1, we consider the equation

$$\frac{d^2v}{d\tau^2} + v^3 = B\cos\tau. \tag{8.1}$$

For the brevity of calculation, we assume that the system is non-dissipative and the non-linearity is given by a cubic function in v.

As for the periodic solution of equation (8.1), we shall here consider the third harmonic as well as the fundamental, and hence put

$$v = y_1\cos\tau + y_3\cos 3\tau. \tag{8.2}$$

Substituting (8.2) into (8.1), and equating terms containing $\cos\tau$ and $\cos 3\tau$ separately to zero, we have

$$\left.\begin{array}{l} y_1\left[\dfrac{3}{4}(y_1^2 + y_1 y_3 + 2y_3^2) - 1\right] = B, \\[2mm] y_3^3 - (12 - 2y_1^2)y_3 + \dfrac{1}{3}y_1^3 = 0. \end{array}\right\} \tag{8.3}$$

Figure 8.1 is obtained by plotting (8.3).

We shall now determine the stability of the equilibrium states illustrated in Fig. 8.1. Proceeding as in the usual manner, the variational equation becomes

$$\frac{d^2\xi}{d\tau^2} + 3v^2\xi = 0. $$

Substitution of the periodic solution (8.2) into the above equation leads to

$$\frac{d^2\xi}{d\tau^2}+\left[\theta_0+2\sum_{s=1}^{3}\theta_s\cos 2s\tau\right]\xi=0\,,$$

where

$$\theta_0=\frac{3}{2}(y_1^2+y_3^2)\,,$$

$$\theta_1=\frac{3}{4}(y_1^2+2y_1y_3)\,,$$

$$\theta_2=\frac{3}{4}y_1y_3\,,$$

$$\theta_3=\frac{3}{4}y_3^2\,.$$

(8.4)

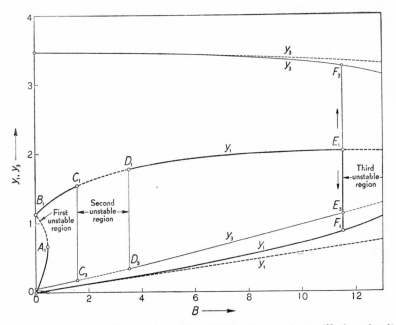

FIG. 8.1. Amplitude characteristic of oscillation in a series-oscillation circuit.

The stability condition in a non-dissipative system may be obtained by putting $\delta=0$ in equation (5.5), i. e.,

$$|\theta_0-n^2|>|\theta_n|.$$

(8.5)

Consequently, if the parameters θ's calculated by substituting the values of y_1, y_3 into (8.4) do not satisfy the condition (8.5), the equilibrium state under consideration is unstable and does not exist actually. We therefore turn to a geometrical discussion on the behavior of the θ's with the stability chart for

Hill's equation. The boundary lines of the stable and unstable regions for Hill's equation are given, to a first approximation, by

$$|\theta_0 - n^2| = |\theta_n|,* \tag{8.6}$$

so that, as illustrated in Fig. 8.2, the straight lines crossing the abscissa at the point n^2 $(n = 1, 2, 3, \cdots)$ with the inclinations of 45° and 135° fix the boundary of the nth unstable region. On the other hand, the loci of θ_n $(n = 1, 2, 3)$ *vs.* θ_0 with varying B are drawn in thick lines in the same figure. Hence, by the condition (8.5), an equilibrium state is unstable when the parameter θ_n lies in the nth unstable region. The unstable states are marked by dotted lines in Fig. 8.1. We shall now consider each unstable region in detail.

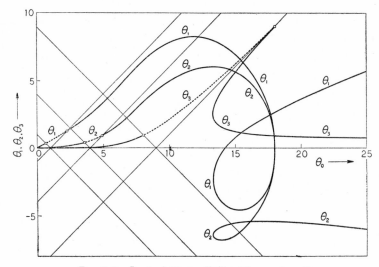

Fɪɢ. 8.2. Loci of θ's in (8.4) with varying B.

(a) When the point (θ_0, θ_1) lies in the first unstable region.

In this case the condition (8.5) fails for $n = 1$. As we have already investigated in Section 6, the stability limits are given by

$$\frac{dB^2}{dr^2} = 0, \quad \text{and} \quad B = 0, \dagger \tag{8.7}$$

which are correlated with the condition that the point (θ_0, θ_1) lies on the boundary lines of the first unstable region in Fig. 8.2, i.e.,

---

* This condition was given by equation (4.10) as the stability criterion for Hill's equation.
† The second condition of (8.7) is added for the non-dissipative case only.

$$\theta_0 = 1 \mp \theta_1 . \tag{8.8}$$

Now, evaluating y_1 and y_3 from (8.3) by the condition (8.7), we obtain

$$
\begin{aligned}
y_1 &= 0.659 , \\
y_3 &= 0.0086 ,
\end{aligned} \Bigg\}
\qquad
\begin{aligned}
y_1 &= 1.128 , \\
y_3 &= 0.0505 .
\end{aligned} \Bigg\}
$$

Upon substituting these values into (8.4), we find that

$$
\begin{aligned}
\theta_0 &= 0.6515, \\
\theta_1 &= 0.3342,
\end{aligned} \Bigg\}
\qquad
\begin{aligned}
\theta_0 &= 1.912, \\
\theta_1 &= 1.040.
\end{aligned} \Bigg\}
$$

It will readily be seen that these values of the parameters do not satisfy the condition (8.8) very closely. This disagreement is due to the deficiency of approximation in deriving the condition (8.8). Since the third harmonic is taken into consideration in the present section, the periodic solution (8.2) affords a better approximation than that in Section 6. Therefore the stability condition must be derived by an approximation of the same order as that of the periodic solution. As we have already mentioned in section 5.3, the condition (8.7) may be obtained by a closer approximation for the stability condition. Thus, for example, if we apply the relation (see Appendix II)

$$\theta_0 = 1 \mp \theta_1 - \frac{1}{8}\theta_1^2 - \frac{1}{6}\theta_2^2 - \frac{1}{16}\theta_3^2 \mp \frac{1}{4}\theta_1\theta_2 \mp \frac{1}{12}\theta_2\theta_3 + \cdots \tag{8.9}$$

instead of (8.8), excellent agreement will result.

(b) When the point (θ_0, θ_2) lies in the second unstable region.

As we see in Fig. 8.2, the locus of θ_2 enters into the second unstable region in the neighborhood of $\theta_0 = 4$. The boundary lines of the second unstable region are given by

$$\theta_0 = 4 \mp \theta_2 , \tag{8.10}$$

and the values of B for which (8.10) holds may readily be found; they are

$$B = 1.576 \quad \text{and} \quad B = 3.529. *$$

As has been explained in Section 5.3 (b), the oscillation accompanied by even harmonics may take place in the second unstable region. †

(c) When the point (θ_0, θ_3) lies in the third unstable region.

---

* See the second unstable region in Fig. 8.1.

† We shall perform some experiments in the following section with regard to this point.

The boundary lines of the third unstable region are given by

$$\theta_0 = 9 \mp \theta_3 . \qquad (8.11)$$

Referring to Fig. 8.1, the amplitude y_1 jumps from E_1 to F_1, and simultaneously the amplitude y_3 from E_3 to F_3 when the parameter θ_3 enters into the third unstable region. This new state is sustained even when B is lowered down to zero, since we have assumed that the system is perfectly non-dissipative. However, this is not the case in practice, and we may suppose that a slight damping in the system will greatly contract the range of this state.

8.2. Experimental investigation

Upon comparing Fig. 8.1 with Fig. 6.2, we see that B is far larger in the

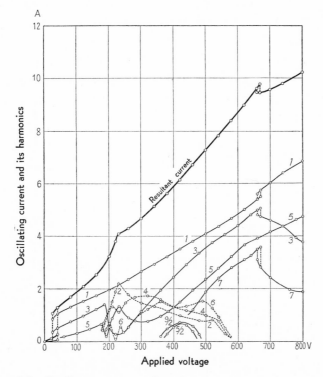

FIG. 8.3. Oscillating current when the iron core is highly saturated.

former case and that the anomalous phenomena due to the second and third regions are likely to occur when B is very large. Since B is proportional to the external force, we shall perform the experiment for the series-oscillation circuit (as illustrated in Fig. 6.1) in which the applied voltage is raised exceedingly.

In Fig. 8.3 the effective value of the oscillating current is plotted (in thick line) for a wide range of the applied voltage. By making use of a heterodyne harmonic analyzer, this current is analyzed into its harmonic components (drawn by fine lines, the numbers on which show the order of the harmonics). The first unstable region ranges between 24 and 40 volts of the applied voltage, and the jump phenomenon in this region is what is usually called the ferro-resonance (see Section 6). The second unstable region extends from 180 to 580

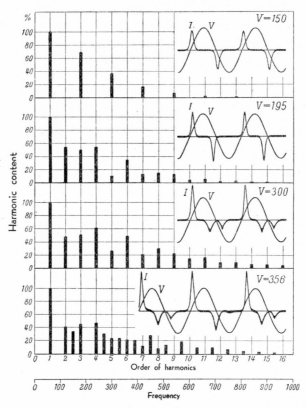

Fɪɢ. 8. 4. Typical wave forms of the oscillating current and their harmonic analysis.

volts. As may be expected from the preceding analysis, the concurrence of even harmonics is a salient feature in this region. The third unstable region occurs above 670 volts, and the oscillation jumps into another stable state. However, owing to the inevitable dissipation in the circuit, this new state is not sustained for such a reduced voltage as shown in Fig. 8.1. Further, in Fig. 8.4, some typical examples of the wave form are illustrated with the percentage content of each harmonic.

In the end we notice that, in order to bring the oscillation into the unstable regions of higher order, the applied voltage must be exceedingly raised, since the series condenser limits the current which magnetizes the reactor core. Therefore we may expect that the higher harmonic oscillation is liable to occur in a parallel-oscillation circuit, and this will be investigated in the following section.

9.1. Higher harmonic oscillations in parallel-oscillation circuits [7, Vol. 30]

Now we consider an electrical circuit as shown in Fig. 9.1, in which two parallel-oscillation circuits are connected in series, each having equal values of L and C respectively. A single oscillation circuit under the impression of an alternating voltage would not present any anomalous phenomenon, since the terminal voltages across L and C are both made equal to the applied voltage.

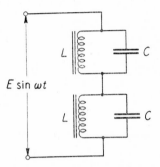

Fig. 9.1. Parallel-oscillation circuit with non-linear inductance.

Denoting the currents in L and C by i_L and i_C respectively, we have

$$n\frac{d\phi}{dt} = \frac{1}{C}\int i_C dt = \frac{1}{2}E\sin\omega t,* \qquad (9.1)$$

where n is the number of turns of the inductance coil and ϕ the magnetic flux in the core. Proceeding in the same manner as in Section 6 (a), we put for the currents, etc.,

$$i_L = I_n \cdot u_L, \quad i_C = I_n \cdot u_C, \quad \phi = \Phi_n \cdot v, \quad \text{and} \quad C = C_n \cdot m, \qquad (9.2)$$

and consider the saturation curve of the form

$$u_L = c_1 v + c_3 v^3, \qquad (9.3)$$

thereupon we may set the relations

$$\left.\begin{array}{l} n\omega^2 C_n \Phi_n = I_n, \\ c_1 + c_3 = 1. \end{array}\right\} \qquad (9.4)$$

Then, by virtue of (9.2) and (9.4), equations (9.1) are transformed to

$$\left.\begin{array}{l} \dfrac{d^2v}{d\tau^2} = \dfrac{1}{m}u_C = B\cos\tau, \\[2mm] \\ \tau = \omega t, \quad B = \dfrac{1}{2}\dfrac{E}{n\omega\Phi_n}. \end{array}\right\} \qquad (9.5)$$

where

---

* It is here assumed that the two oscillation circuits behave just in the same way, so that each circuit is impressed by one-half of the applied voltage. We shall shortly investigate the stability of this state.

Hence the equilibrium state is readily obtained as

$$v = y \cos \tau = -B \cos \tau . \tag{9.6}$$

We shall now consider the stability problem. Let the variations of u_L, u_C, and v in one of the oscillation circuits be δu_L, δu_C, and ξ respectively. Then corresponding variations $-\delta u_L$, $-\delta u_C$, and $-\xi$ will result in the other oscillation

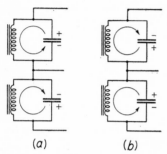

circuit. Upon applying Kirchhoff's first law to the junction point of the two oscillation circuits, we have

$$\delta u_L + \delta u_C = 0 . \tag{9.7}$$

Hence, as indicated in Fig. 9.2, the currents due to this perturbation flow in both circuits with opposite sense, and do not come out to the external source.

(a)   (b)

FIG. 9.2. Direction of oscillation caused by perturbation.

From (9.3), δu_L and ξ are interrelated by

$$\delta u_L = (c_1 + 3c_3 v^2)\, \xi . \tag{9.8}$$

Substituting (9.7), (9.8) into (9.5), we have

$$\frac{d^2\xi}{d\tau^2} + \frac{1}{m}(c_1 + 3c_3 v^2)\, \xi = 0 .$$

Further, substituting the periodic solution (9.6), we obtain the equation of Mathieu's type, i.e.,

where

$$\left.\begin{array}{l} \dfrac{d^2\xi}{d\tau^2} + (\theta_0 + 2\theta_1 \cos 2\tau)\, \xi = 0 , \\[2ex] \theta_0 = \dfrac{1}{m}\left(c_1 + \dfrac{3}{2}c_3 y^2\right), \\[2ex] \theta_1 = \dfrac{1}{m}\dfrac{3}{4}c_3 y^2 . \end{array}\right\} \tag{9.9}$$

Now we see that the equilibrium state (9.6) becomes unstable when (9.9) has an unstable solution, and that the higher harmonic oscillation (mostly the nth harmonic) will be excited when the point (θ_0, θ_1) lies in the nth unstable region of the stability chart.

As mentioned in Section 8.1, the higher harmonic oscillation is likely to occur when θ_0 is increased. In our present case, as noticed in (9.9), this will be effected by decreasing m or increasing y, the latter being proportional to B by (9.6). In the series-oscillation circuit, however, we have the relation from (6.9), *viz.*,

$$c_3\left(\frac{3}{4}y^3 - y\right) = B, \quad \text{when} \quad k = 0,$$

so that, increase in y would require an excessive value for B. Therefore the higher harmonic oscillation may take place with a comparatively lower voltage in the parallel-oscillation circuit. This agrees with the physical consideration that we have noticed at the end of Section 8.2.

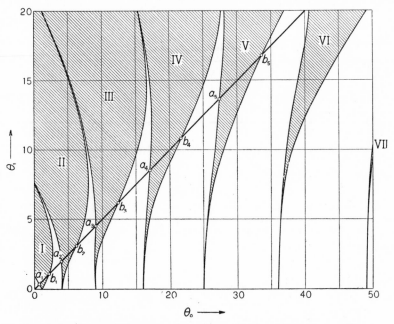

FIG. 9.3. Locus of the point (θ_0, θ_1) in (9.10) with varying B^2/m.

We are now to determine the region in which the higher harmonic oscillation is excited. For the brevity of calculation, taking the particular case of

$$c_1 = 0, \quad \text{and} \quad c_3 = 1,$$

we obtain the following relation for the parameters θ_0 and θ_1 in (9.9); i.e.,

$$\theta_0 = 2\theta_1 = \frac{3}{2}\frac{B^2}{m}. \tag{9.10}$$

In Fig. 9.3 the locus of the point (θ_0, θ_1) is drawn (in thick line) by varying B^2/m. The unstable regions of orders 1, 2, 3, ⋯ for Mathieu's equation are also illustrated by the areas I, II, III, ⋯ respectively (see Fig. 3.1). Hence we see that the locus (a straight line in this case) passes alternately the regions of stability and instability with the increase of B^2/m. If we denote the intersecting points of the locus with the boundary of the nth unstable region by a_n and b_n (as marked in the figure), and further, the corresponding values of θ_0 by θ_{an} and θ_{bn} respectively, we may determine in B, m-plane the boundary curves of the nth region in which the nth harmonic is mostly excited; they are given by

$$\frac{3}{2}\frac{B^2}{m} = \theta_{an}, \quad \text{and} \quad \frac{3}{2}\frac{B^2}{m} = \theta_{bn}. \tag{9.11}$$

The particular values of the parameters θ_{an}, θ_{bn} are readily obtained from Fig. 9.3, and are shown in Table 9.1.

TABLE 9.1. Values of θ_{an} and θ_{bn} in (9.11).

n	1	2	3	4	5	6
θ_{an}	0.66	3.71	9.24	17.27	27.76	40.66
θ_{bn}	1.78	6.10	12.88	22.00	33.82	47.80

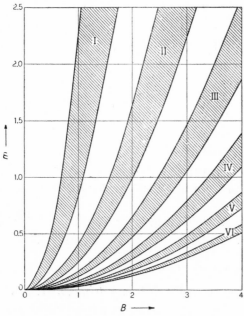

Fɪɢ. 9.4. Regions of self-excitation of the higher harmonic oscillations (calculated).

Substituting these values into (9.11), the regions of the higher harmonic oscillations are depicted in Fig. 9.4.*

9.2. Experimental investigation

We first perform experiments on the circuit as illustrated in Fig. 9.1. Since B and m are proportional to the applied voltage and the capacitance respectively, we seek, by varying these quantities, the regions in which the higher harmonics are excited. The result is depicted in Fig. 9.5, in which the numerals I, II, III, ⋯ correspond to those in Fig. 9.4. The wave form of the condenser current I_C with

* The numerals I, II, III, ⋯ in each region correspond to those of Fig. 9.3.

reference to the applied voltage is also illustrated in the figure, showing that their principal frequencies are 1, 2, 3, ··· times the impressed frequency.

As a result of the excitation of such a harmonic, the potential of the junction point of the two oscillation circuits oscillates with respect to the neutral point of the applied voltage with the frequency of that harmonic. In Fig. 9.6, the

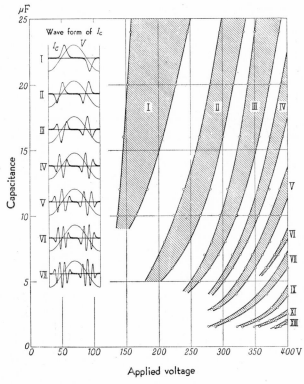

Fig. 9.5. Regions of self-excitation of the higher harmonic oscillations (experimental).

anomalous neutral voltage V_n is illustrated against the applied voltage.† We see in the figure that once the self-excitation is started, it may be stopped by decreasing the applied voltage to a value which is lower than before. The preceding analysis gives no consideration to this hysteresis phenomenon, since, when the self-excitation is built up to some extent, the circuit condition is quite altered, and so the analysis which assumes the equilibrium state (9.6) will no

---

† The self-excited oscillation in the first unstable region (marked by I) has the same frequency as that of the applied voltage, and this phenomenon is what is called the "neutral inversion" in electric transmission lines.

longer apply.‡ It should also be mentioned that the regions in Fig. 9.5 are those in which the self-excitation starts and as a matter of fact the oscillation may be sustained in certain regions exterior to the hatched regions.

In Fig. 9.7, the effective value of the condenser current is plotted (in thick lines) against the applied voltage. This current is further analyzed into its

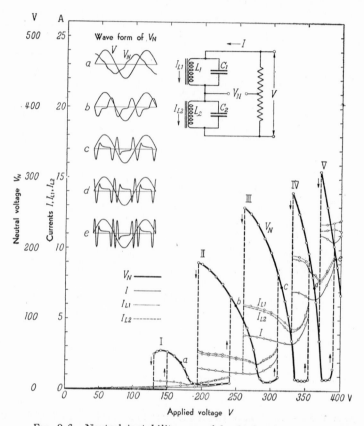

FIG. 9.6. Neutral instability caused by higher harmonic excitation.

harmonic components (drawn by fine lines, the numbers on which show the order of the harmonics). Hence we see that the odd harmonics are present in the regions of odd orders, i.e., in I, III, V, ⋯; on the other hand, the even harmonics are present in the regions of even orders, i.e., in II, IV, VI, ⋯. This is in excellent accordance with the theory of Mathieu's equation, as we may expect from the form of the unstable solutions in Section 3.3.

Further, it may be conjectured that when the alternating voltage is applied

‡ We shall have the opportunity to discuss this point in detail and determine the ultimate amplitude of the self-excited oscillation.

on the circuit, the self-excited oscillation would gradually be built up with increasing amplitude, taking the form

$$e^{\mu\tau}[\sin(n\tau-\sigma)+\cdots], \quad \text{with} \quad \mu>0,$$

and ultimately get to the steady state with constant amplitude which is limited

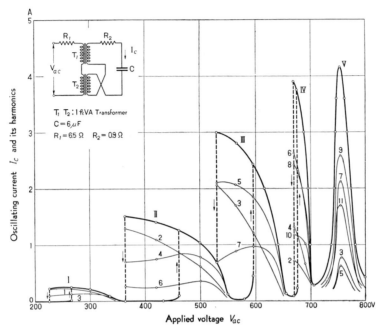

FIG. 9.7. Higher harmonic oscillations and their harmonic analysis.

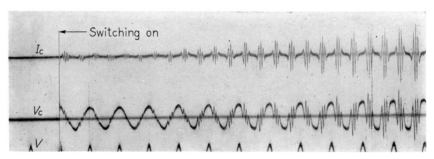

V: applied voltage V_C: voltage across condenser I_C: current through condenser

FIG. 9. 8. Building up of a self-excited oscillation.

by the non-linear characteristic of the circuit. This is verified by experiments. An example of such transient states is given in Fig. 9.8, showing the building up of the seventh harmonic oscillation correlated with the seventh unstable region for Mathieu's equation.

Finally it is mentioned that when the self-excitation of these oscillations is undesirable, the following procedure will effectively prevent it. Namely, we couple the secondary coils to the respective reactors as illustrated in Fig. 9.9, and connect them in series but with opposite polarity. Then, since the anomalous oscillation is excited in the primary oscillation circuits with opposite direction (see Fig. 9.2), induced voltage in the secondary coils have the same direction and a short circuit results, thus preventing the building up of the anomalous oscillation. On the other hand, the forced current due to the applied voltage flows through the primary coils in the same direction and induces no current in the secondary circuit. Therefore this secondary circuit is effective only in preventing the anomalous oscillation and exert no influence upon the primary forced current.

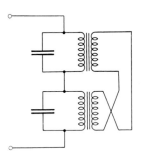

FIG. 9.9.   Suppression of self-excited oscillation.

CHAPTER IV

SUBHARMONIC OSCILLATIONS

10. Introduction

In the foregoing two chapters, we investigated the harmonic and the higher harmonic oscillations whose fundamental frequency was equal to that of the external force. We are now to deal with the subharmonic oscillations whose fundamental frequency is a fraction $1/\nu$ ($\nu = 2, 3, 4, \cdots$) of that of the external force. As we have briefly referred to in Section 1, these oscillations are of another important type in the field of non-linear oscillations, and frequently occur in various branches of engineering and physical sciences [8, 9, 12, 21, 23, 24, 32, 46, 47, 51].

We first take the fundamental equation

$$\frac{d^2v}{d\tau^2} + 2\delta \frac{dv}{d\tau} + f(v) = B \cos \nu\tau , \qquad (10.1)$$

in which 2δ is a constant damping coefficient and $f(v)$ a term characterizing the non-linear restoring force. It will be noticed that, since the period of the external force is $2\pi/\nu$, the subharmonic oscillation of order $1/\nu$ has a period 2π and may be expressed by a linear combination of $\sin \tau$ and $\cos \tau$.

In the following sections, we shall first investigate the relationship between the non-linear characteristics expressed by the term $f(v)$ and the order $1/\nu$ of the subharmonic oscillations. Then the subharmonic oscillations of orders $1/3$ and $1/2$ will be investigated in particular with special attention directed to the stability of the periodic oscillation.*

11. Relationship between the non-linear characteristics and the order of subharmonic oscillations

In order to investigate this we shall consider the following polynomial for the restoring force $f(v)$, i.e.,

$$f(v) = c_1 v + c_2 v^2 + c_3 v^3 + \cdots , \qquad (11.1)$$

---

* The discussion, throughout the present chapter, is confined to the steady states of oscillation. The discussion on the transient states will be given later in Chapter VI.

where c_1, c_2, c_3, $\cdots$ are constants determined by the non-linear characteristics. As in the case of the harmonic oscillations [see equation (6.4)], these constants may be subjected, without loss of generality, to the condition

$$c_1 + c_2 + c_3 + \cdots = 1 . \qquad (11.2)$$

In so far as we deal with the steady states of oscillation, the periodic solution of equation (10.1) may be expressed by

$$v = v_0 + x \sin \tau + y \cos \tau + w \cos \nu\tau , \qquad (11.3)$$

in which the constant term v_0, the subharmonic oscillation $x \sin \tau + y \cos \tau$, and the oscillation having the impressed frequency $w \cos \nu\tau$ are considered on account of their prime importance.* Following Mandelstam and Papalexi [21, p. 227], the amplitude w may further be approximated by

$$w = \frac{1}{1-\nu^2} B . \qquad (11.4)$$

This approximation is legitimate in the case when the non-linearity is small. But, as will be shown later, the relation (11.4) is a fairly good approximation even when the departure from linearity is large.

Substituting (11.3) into (10.1), and equating the coefficients of $\sin \tau$ and $\cos \tau$ separately to zero, we have the following cases according to the form of the non-linear characteristics (11.1).

Case 1. When the non-linearity is given by $f(v) = c_1 v + c_3 v^3$

Under circumstances when the non-linearity is symmetrical, i. e., $f(v)$ is odd in v, the constant term v_0 in equation (11.3) is usually discarded, and, for $\nu = 2, 4, 5, \cdots$, the above-mentioned substitution leads to

$$\left.\begin{aligned}
\left[1 - \frac{3}{4}(x^2 + y^2) - \frac{3}{2} w^2\right] x + ky = 0 , \\[2mm]
\left[1 - \frac{3}{4}(x^2 + y^2) - \frac{3}{2} w^2\right] y - kx = 0 ,
\end{aligned}\right\} \qquad (11.5)$$

where $k = 2\delta/c_3$. Multiplying the first equation by y, the second by x, and subtracting the second product from the first, we obtain

$$k(x^2 + y^2) = 0 .$$

---

* It is tacitly assumed that the damping coefficient 2δ is not so large that the term containing $\sin \nu\tau$ may be omitted in equation (11.3).

This means that the amplitude of the subharmonic oscillation is zero as long as the damping is present (i. e., $k \neq 0$). Hence the subharmonic oscillations of orders $1/2$, $1/4$, $1/5$, $\cdots$ cannot occur in this case. However, as will be investigated in the following section, real roots of x and y which are not simultaneously zero may be obtained in the case when $\nu = 3$, and some of them are maintained in stable states.† Hence, the conclusion that the subharmonic oscillation of order $1/3$ may occur in the case when the non-linear term $c_3 v^3$ is contained in equation (11.1).

Case. 2. When the non-linearity is given by $f(v) = c_1 v + c_2 v^2 + c_3 v^3$

The non-linearity is unsymmetrical, and the constant term v_0 in equation (11.3) must be considered. The subharmonic oscillation of order $1/2$ occurs predominantly in this case. The detailed investigation will be carried out later in Sections 13. 1 and 13. 2.‡

Case 3. When the non-linearity is given by $f(v) = c_1 v + c_5 v^5$

Although the non-linear term $c_3 v^3$ is absent in this case, the subharmonic oscillation of order $1/3$ is maintained. The detailed investigation will be given in Section 12. 2. The subharmonic oscillation of order $1/5$ is also maintained in this case.

From the foregoing considerations, it may be deduced in general that the presence of the term $c_\nu v^\nu$ in equation (11.1) is the sufficient condition for the occurrence of the subharmonic oscillation of order $1/\nu$. However, this is not the necessary condition as we notice in Case 3. It may also be concluded that the subharmonic oscillation of order $1/\nu$ does not occur when the highest degree of the power of the non-linear terms in equation (11.1) is less than ν.

Finally, in order to get familiar with the subharmonic oscillations, some oscillograms illustrating those of different orders are shown in Fig. 11.1. These wave forms are obtained by using an electrical circuit consisting of a saturable core inductance in series with a condenser across an alternating current source [8].

---

† These real roots represent the states of equilibrium which are not always sustained, but are only able to last as long as they are stable.

‡ It is only mentioned here that, by a closer investigation in which the term v_0 is taken into account, the subharmonic oscillation of order $1/2$ may scarcely take place even in the case when $c_2 = 0$ in equation (11.1). This result is also verified by experiments, though the range of occurrence is considerably restricted. Therefore, strictly speaking, the conclusion in Case 1 should be modified in this respect.

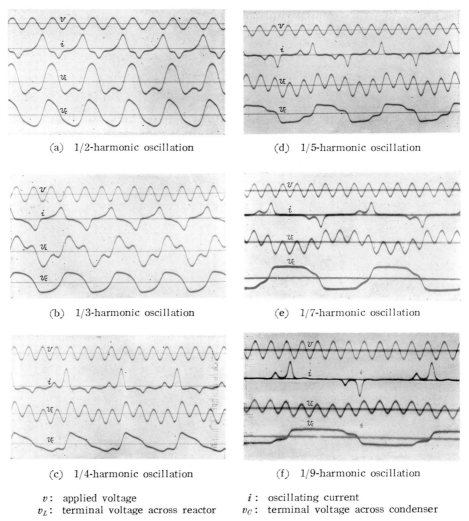

(a) 1/2-harmonic oscillation

(d) 1/5-harmonic oscillation

(b) 1/3-harmonic oscillation

(e) 1/7-harmonic oscillation

(c) 1/4-harmonic oscillation

(f) 1/9-harmonic oscillation

v: applied voltage i: oscillating current
v_L: terminal voltage across reactor v_C: terminal voltage across condenser

Fig. 11.1. Wave forms of subharmonic oscillations.

12.1. Subharmonic oscillation of order 1/3 with the non-linear characteristic $u = c_1 v + c_3 v^3$ [12]

We shall first investigate the subharmonic oscillation of order 1/3 in detail.

(a) Non-dissipative case

Putting

$$\nu = 3, \qquad k = 0,$$
$$c_2 = c_4 = c_5 = \cdots = 0,$$

in equations (10.1) and (11.1), and remembering the condition (11.2), we have the following equation for the subharmonic oscillation of order 1/3, i.e.,

$$\frac{d^2v}{d\tau^2} + v = c_3\,(v-v^3) + B\cos 3\tau\,. \tag{12.1}$$

By the use of equation (11.4), the periodic solution will be given by

$$v = x\sin\tau + y\cos\tau + w\cos 3\tau\,,$$

with

$$w = \frac{1}{1-3^2}\,B = -\frac{1}{8}\,B\,. \tag{12.2}$$

Substituting (12.2) into (12.1), and equating the coefficients of $\sin\tau$ and $\cos\tau$ separately to zero, we have

$$
\begin{aligned}
\left[1-\frac{3}{4}\,(x^2+y^2)-\frac{3}{2}\,w^2\right]x &= -\frac{3w}{4}\,2xy\,, \\
\left[1-\frac{3}{4}\,(x^2+y^2)-\frac{3}{2}\,w^2\right]y &= -\frac{3w}{4}\,(x^2-y^2)\,.
\end{aligned}
\tag{12.3}
$$

Multiplying the first equation by y, the second by x, and subtracting the products so formed, we obtain

$$x = 0 \quad\text{or}\quad x = \pm\sqrt{3}\,y\,.$$

For each value of x we have two pairs of roots, hence we obtain six pairs of equilibrium states in all. But we are satisfied with the investigation of the equilibrium states only for which $x = 0$, because, as will be shown later, the other states have the same amplitude, but differ in phase by $2\pi/3$ or $4\pi/3$ radians in τ, *viz.*, one or two complete cycles of the applied force. This is a plausible result since we are concerned with the subharmonic oscillation of order 1/3.

For $x = 0$, assuming that $y \neq 0$ in the second equation of (12.3), we obtain

$$y^2 + yw + 2w^2 - \frac{4}{3} = 0\,. \tag{12.4}$$

This equation shows the relationship between the amplitude w (which is here assumed to be proportional to the external force B) and the amplitude y of the subharmonic oscillation and is plotted as a part of an ellipse in Fig. 12.1.

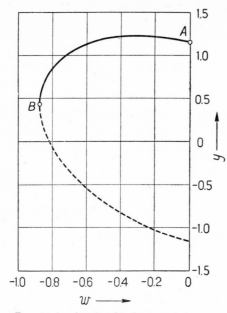

FIG. 12.1. Amplitude characteristic
of the 1/3-harmonic oscillation
(non-linearity by cubic function).

We are now to determine the stability of the equilibrium states given by equation (12.4). Proceeding in the usual manner, the variation ξ from the equilibrium states will satisfy the equation

$$\frac{d^2\xi}{d\tau^2}+(c_1+3c_3v^2)\,\xi=0\,.$$

Substituting into this the equilibrium states represented by

$$v = y\cos\tau+w\cos 3\tau\,,$$

the following equation of Hill's type is derived, i. e.,

$$\frac{d^2\xi}{d\tau^2}+[\theta_0+2\theta_1\cos 2\tau+2\theta_2\cos 4\tau+2\theta_3\cos 6\tau]\,\xi=0\,,$$

where

$$\theta_0 = c_1+\frac{3}{2}\,c_3\,(y^2+w^2)\,,$$

$$\theta_1 = \frac{3}{4}\,c_3\,(y^2+2yw)\,,$$

$$\theta_2 = \frac{3}{2}\,c_3yw\,,$$

$$\theta_3 = \frac{3}{4}\,c_3w^2\,.$$

(12.5)

Since w and y are determined by equations (12.2) and (12.4) respectively, the parameters θ's in equations (12.5) may readily be calculated.

The stability condition in the non-dissipative system is given by putting $\delta=0$ in equation (5.5), i. e.,

$$(\theta_0-n^2+\theta_n)(\theta_0-n^2-\theta_n)>0\,,$$

or

$$|\theta_n|<|\theta_0-n^2|\,,\qquad (n=1,\,2,\,3,\,\cdots)\,.$$

(12.6)

The condition for $n = 1$ determines the stability against building up of the unstable oscillation whose principal frequency is the same as that of the subharmonic. By the use of equations (12.4) and (12.5), this leads to

$$2y > -w. \tag{12.7}$$

Hence, the equilibrium states represented by the dotted-line curve in Fig. 12.1 are unstable and do not exist actually. Figure 12.2 shows the loci of θ_n ($n = 1, 2, 3$)

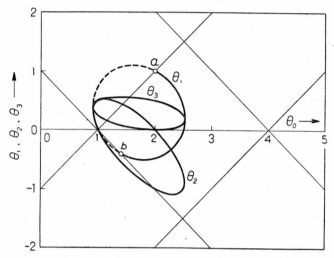

Fig. 12.2. Loci of θ's in (12.5) with varying w.

which are drawn by varying the value of w (or B) for the limiting case of $c_1 = 0$ and $c_3 = 1$. As expected from the stability condition for $n = 1$, θ_1 enters into the first unstable region in the dotted-line interval ab. At the critical points a and b,

$$2y = -w,$$

and these points correspond respectively to A and B in Fig. 12.1. It is clear from Fig. 12.2 that neither θ_2 nor θ_3 enters into its corresponding unstable region. Thus we see that, since the conditions (12.6) for $n = 2$ and $n = 3$ are satisfied, only the condition (12.7) is sufficient to determine the stability in this case.* Hence, in the end, we may conclude that the part of the curve

---

* If θ_n ($n \geqq 2$) enters into the nth unstable region, the unstable oscillation of order $n/3$ will take place. If this oscillation grows to be predominant, the original subharmonic oscillation of order 1/3 will no longer be maintained. An example for such a case ($n = 2$) will be given later in Section 12.2.

(in Fig. 12.1) which lies between A and B represents the stable oscillations.

(b) Dissipative case

When the damping is considered in a non-linear system, the fundamental equation takes the form

$$\frac{d^2v}{d\tau^2} + 2\delta\frac{dv}{d\tau} + c_1v + c_3v^3 = B\cos 3\tau , \tag{12.8}$$

and the periodic solution is expressed by

$$v = x\sin\tau + y\cos\tau + w\cos 3\tau ,$$

with

$$w = -\frac{B}{8} . \tag{12.9}$$

Substituting (12.9) into (12.8), and equating the coefficients of $\sin\tau$ and $\cos\tau$ separately to zero, we have

$$Ax + ky = -\frac{3w}{4}\,2xy ,$$

$$Ay - kx = -\frac{3w}{4}\,(x^2 - y^2) ,$$

where

$$A = 1 - \frac{3}{4}\,(x^2 + y^2) - \frac{3}{2}\,w^2 ,$$

$$k = \frac{2\delta}{c_3} . \tag{12.10}$$

Squaring and adding the first two equations, we obtain

$$A^2 + k^2 = \left(\frac{3w}{4}\right)^2 r^2 , \qquad r^2 = x^2 + y^2 , \tag{12.11}$$

or, by putting $r^2 = R$ and $w^2 = W$,

$$\frac{9}{16}R^2 + \left(\frac{27}{16}W - \frac{3}{2}\right)R + \left(\frac{9}{4}W^2 - 3W + k^2 + 1\right) = 0 . \tag{12.12}$$

Hence the relationship between W and R, and consequently the amplitude of the subharmonic oscillation are determined, and the result is depicted in Fig. 12.3 a, b for several values of k.

The components x, y of the amplitude r may readily be obtained as follows. By equations (12.10) and (12.11), we have

$$x^3 - \frac{3}{4} Rx - \frac{kR}{3w} = 0,$$

and

$$y^3 - \frac{3}{4} Ry - \frac{AR}{3w} = 0.$$

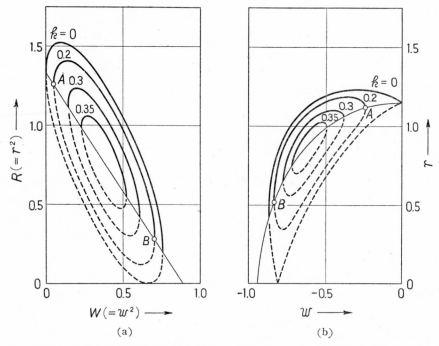

Fɪɢ. 12.3a. Relationship between W and R in (12.12).   b. Amplitude characteristic of the 1/3-harmonic oscillation.

Hence the components x, y are given by

$$\left.\begin{array}{l}
x = -r\cos\theta, \quad -r\cos(\theta + 120°), \quad -r\cos(\theta + 240°), \\[4pt]
y = -r\sin\theta, \quad -r\sin(\theta + 120°), \quad -r\sin(\theta + 240°),
\end{array}\right\}$$

where

$$\cos 3\theta = -\frac{4k}{3wr}.$$

(12.13)

The stability problem may be treated in the same manner as in the preceding case. The equation which characterizes the small variation ξ is given by

$$\frac{d^2\xi}{d\tau^2} + 2\delta\frac{d\xi}{d\tau} + (c_1 + 3c_3 v^2)\,\xi = 0\,.$$

By the well-known transformation $\xi = e^{-\delta\tau}\cdot\eta$, this leads to

$$\frac{d^2\eta}{d\tau^2} + [c_1 - \delta^2 + 3c_3 v^2]\,\eta = 0\,.$$

Substituting into this the periodic solution (12.9), we obtain the following Hill's equation, i. e.,

$$\frac{d^2\eta}{d\tau^2} + [\theta_0 + 2\theta_1 \cos(2\tau - \varepsilon_1) + 2\theta_2 \cos(4\tau - \varepsilon_2)$$

$$+ 2\theta_3 \cos(6\tau - \varepsilon_3)]\,\eta = 0\,,$$

where

$$\theta_0 = c_1 - \delta^2 + \frac{3}{2}\,c_3\,(x^2 + y^2 + w^2)\,,$$

$$\theta_n^2 = \theta_{ns}^2 + \theta_{nc}^2\,, \qquad \varepsilon_n = \arctan\frac{\theta_{ns}}{\theta_{nc}}\,, \qquad (n = 1,\,2,\,3)\,, \qquad\qquad (12.14)$$

$$\theta_{1s} = \frac{3}{2}\,c_3 x(y - w)\,, \qquad \theta_{1c} = \frac{3}{4}\,c_3\,(-x^2 + y^2 + 2yw)\,,$$

$$\theta_{2s} = \frac{3}{2}\,c_3 xw\,, \qquad\qquad \theta_{2c} = \frac{3}{2}\,c_3 yw\,,$$

$$\theta_{3s} = 0\,, \qquad\qquad\qquad \theta_{3c} = \frac{3}{4}\,c_3 w^2\,.$$

The stability condition in the dissipative system is given by

$$(\theta_0 - n^2)^2 + 2(\theta_0 + n^2)\,\delta^2 + \delta^4 > \theta_n^2\,, \qquad (n = 1,\,2,\,3,\,\cdots)\,. \qquad (12.15)$$

The condition for $n = 1$ is obtained by substituting θ_0 and θ_1 of (12.14) into (12.15), and further by virtue of (12.10) and (12.12), we ultimately find

$$R + \frac{3}{2}\,W - \frac{4}{3} > 0\,. \qquad\qquad (12.16)$$

Hence the equilibrium states represented by the dotted-line curves in Fig. 12.3 are unstable and do not actually exist. Figure 12.4 shows the loci of θ_n $(n = 1, 2, 3)$ which are drawn by varying the value of w (or B) for the case of $c_1 = 0$, $c_3 = 1$, and $\delta = 0.1$. As illustrated in the figure, the boundary curve of the first unstable region is given by a hyperbola,* and θ_1 enters into this region in the dotted-line

---

* In the case when $\delta = 0$, this hyperbola is reduced to the straight lines (drawn by chain lines in Fig. 12.4) which intersect the abscissa at the point $(1, 0)$ (see Fig. 12.2).

interval *ab*. At the critical points *a* and *b*, we have

$$R + \frac{3}{2}W - \frac{4}{3} = 0,$$

and these points correspond, respectively, to *A* and *B* in Fig. 12.3. It is also obvious from Fig. 12.4 that neither θ_2 nor θ_3 enters into its corresponding unstable region. Hence, in the end, the condition (12.16) for $n = 1$ is sufficient to determine the stability of equilibrium states in the case when the non-linearity is characterized by a cubic function.

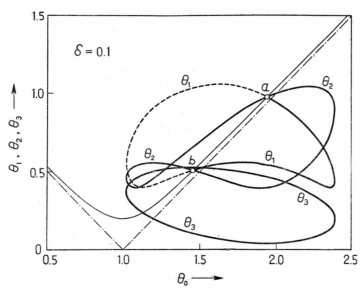

FIG. 12.4. Loci of θ's in (12.14) with varying w.

(c) Some remarks on the approximation in the preceding analysis

As shown in Fig. 12.1 or 12.3, the stable range of equilibrium states is interposed between the critical points *A* and *B* at which *w* has its limiting values. Since *w* is proportional to *B* by equation (12.2) or (12.9), these stability limits are obtained when the external force also has its limiting values. This is a plausible result from the physical point of view.

However, as mentioned before, the approximation (11.4) is reasonable as long as the non-linearity is small, *viz.*, $c_3 \ll c_1$ in the foregoing analysis. Thus, it might seem improper to apply this assumption in the case when $c_1 = 0$ and $c_3 = 1$. But it will be explained below that the relation (11.4) may be applied with a fairly good approximation even when the non-linearity is predominant, and also that the stability limits mentioned above are given by the condition that the external force B has its limiting values.

For the sake of simplicity, we consider the non-dissipative case. Putting $c_1 = 0$, $c_3 = 1$ in equation (12.1), we have

$$\frac{d^2v}{d\tau^2} + v^3 = B \cos 3\tau .$$

Substituting the periodic solution

$$v = y \cos \tau + w \cos 3\tau ,$$

and equating the coefficients of $\cos \tau$ and $\cos 3\tau$ separately to zero, we obtain

$$\left.\begin{aligned} y^2 + yw + 2w^2 - \frac{4}{3} &= 0 , \\ \frac{1}{4} y^3 + \frac{3}{2} y^2 w + \frac{3}{4} w^3 - 9w &= B . \end{aligned}\right\} \quad (12.17)$$

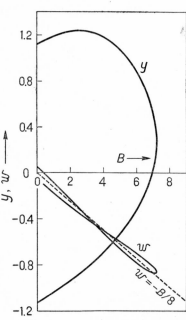

Fig. 12.5. Relationship between y, w and B in (12.17).

Figure 12.5 is obtained by plotting (12.17). Thus we see that the approximation $w = -B/8$ may be applied without serious error. It is also noticed that, since B is no longer proportional to w, the limiting values of B and w do not take place simultaneously.

We shall next show that the stability limits are given by the limiting values of B, or in other words, the parameters θ's in Hill's equation (12.5) have the characteristic values when $B = 0$ or $B = $ maximum.* For these limiting values of B, the values of y and w are calculated by (12.17), and the parameters θ's are found from (12.5). They are shown in Table 12.1.

TABLE 12.1.† Values of y, w, and the θ's for $B = 0$ and $B = $ max.

B	y	w	θ_0	θ_1	θ_2	θ_3
0	1.127	0.0510	1.9092	1.0392	0.0862	0.0019
Max.$=7.205$	0.284	-0.8655	1.2443	-0.3078	-0.3681	0.5619

† For the case in which the non-linear characteristic is given by a cubic function.

* In the case when the non-dissipative system is considered, the characteristic exponent in the solution of Hill's equation becomes zero at the stability limits.

The boundary of the first unstable region is given by equations (12.6), namely,

$$\theta_0 = 1 \pm \theta_1 . \qquad (12.18)$$

Substituting the values of θ_1 of Table 12.1, we obtain

$$\left. \begin{array}{l} \theta_0 = 2.0392 \quad \text{for} \quad B = 0 , \\ \theta_0 = 1.3078 \quad \text{for} \quad B = \text{max.} \end{array} \right\}$$

These values differ from those given in Table 12.1 by 6.8 percent and 5.1 percent respectively. This is due to the deficiency of approximation in equation (12.18). Hence, for the accurate values of y, w calculated by equations (12.17), we have to apply the closer approximation given, for example, by the development †

$$\left. \begin{array}{l} \theta_0 = 1 \pm \theta_1 - \dfrac{1}{8}\theta_1^2 - \dfrac{1}{6}\theta_2^2 - \dfrac{1}{16}\theta_3^2 \pm \dfrac{1}{4}\theta_1\theta_2 \pm \dfrac{1}{12}\theta_2\theta_3 \\[2mm] \mp \dfrac{1}{64}\theta_1^3 + \dfrac{1}{48}\theta_1^2\theta_2 \pm \dfrac{5}{192}\theta_1^2\theta_3 \mp \dfrac{1}{144}\theta_1\theta_2^2 \\[2mm] \mp \dfrac{1}{2304}\theta_1\theta_3^2 \pm \dfrac{1}{48}\theta_2^2\theta_3 - \dfrac{13}{288}\theta_1\theta_2\theta_3 + \cdots . \end{array} \right\} \qquad (12.19)$$

Now, substituting the values of $\theta_1 \sim \theta_3$ of Table 12.1 into equation (12.19), we obtain

$$\left. \begin{array}{l} \theta_0 = 1.9038 \quad \text{for} \quad B = 0 , \\ \theta_0 = 1.2352 \quad \text{for} \quad B = \text{max.,} \end{array} \right\}$$

which differ from the values given in Table 12.1 by 0.28 percent and 0.73 percent respectively. Thus the discrepancies are much reduced, and we may conclude that the stability limits are given by the condition that the external force B has its limiting values.‡

12.2. Subharmonic oscillation of order 1/3 with the non-linear characteristic $u = c_1 v + c_5 v^5$ [12]

For the brevity of calculation, we consider the non-dissipative case only. Putting

---

† This relation is obtained by putting $\sigma = 0$ and $\sigma = -\pi/2$ in equation (II.4) in Appendix II.

‡ As mentioned in Section 5.3, it is not difficult to show that the stability limits are exactly given by the condition $dB/dr = 0$ (and $B = 0$ in a non-dissipative case), provided that the order of approximation assumed in deriving the stability condition is the same as that assumed for the periodic solution.

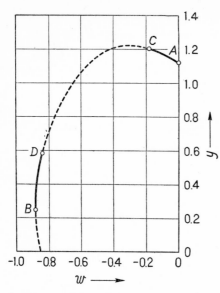

FIG. 12.6. Amplitude characteristic of the 1/3-harmonic oscillation (non-linearity by quintic function).

$$\nu = 3, \qquad \delta = 0,$$

and

$$c_2 = c_3 = c_4 = c_6 = \cdots = 0,$$

in equations (10.1) and (11.1), and remembering the condition (11.2), we have

$$\frac{d^2v}{d\tau^2} + v = c_5 (v - v^5) + B \cos 3\tau. \quad (12.20)$$

Substituting the periodic solution

$$v = y \cos \tau + w \cos 3\tau, \quad w = -B/8,$$

into (12.20), and equating to zero the coefficient of $\cos \tau$, we obtain

$$y^4 + \frac{5}{2} y^3 w + 6 y^2 w^2 + 3 y w^3 + 3 w^4 - \frac{8}{5} = 0. \quad (12.21)$$

The relationship between y and w is illustrated in Fig. 12.6. Negative values of y are omitted in the figure, because, as will be shown later, the equilibrium states in this part are unstable.

The stability problem may be treated in the same manner as in the preceding section, and the variational equation leads to the following Hill's equation, namely,

$$\frac{d^2\xi}{d\tau^2} + \left[\theta_0 + 2 \sum_{s=1}^{6} \theta_s \cos 2s\tau \right] \xi = 0,$$

where

$$\theta_0 = c_1 + \frac{5}{8} c_5 (3y^4 + 4y^3 w + 12 y^2 w^2 + 3w^4),$$

$$\theta_1 = \frac{5}{4} c_5 (y^4 + 3y^3 w + 3y^2 w^2 + 3yw^3),$$

$$\theta_2 = \frac{5}{16} c_5 (y^4 + 12 y^3 w + 6 y^2 w^2 + 12 yw^3),$$

$$\theta_3 = \frac{5}{4} c_5 (y^3 w + 3 y^2 w^2 + w^4),$$

$$\theta_4 = \frac{5}{8} c_5 (3 y^2 w^2 + 2 yw^3),$$

$$\theta_5 = \frac{5}{4} c_5 yw^3,$$

$$\theta_6 = \frac{5}{16} c_5 w^4.$$

$$(12.22)$$

The stability condition for $n = 1$ is obtained by substituting θ_0 and θ_1 into (12.6). Further by virtue of (12.21), we ultimately find

$$y^3 + \frac{15}{8} y^2 w + 3 y w^2 + \frac{3}{4} w^3 > 0 , \quad \text{for} \quad w < 0 . \tag{12.23}$$

Referring to Fig. 12.6, the equilibrium states in the interval between A and B satisfy the condition (12.23). The stability limits A and B are given by the conditions $w = 0$ and $w = \text{max.}$ respectively.

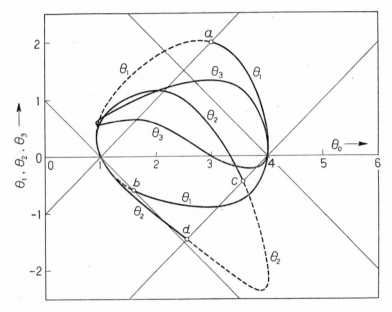

Fᴵɢ. 12.7.   Loci of θ's in (12.22) with varying w.

Figure 12.7 shows the loci of θ_n ($n = 1, 2, 3$) which are drawn by varying the value of w (or B) for the limiting case of $c_1 = 0$ and $c_5 = 1$. As expected from the stability condition for $n = 1$, θ_1 enters into the first unstable region in the dotted-line interval ab. We see moreover that θ_2 enters into the second unstable region in the dotted-line interval cd. Hence the stability condition for $n = 2$ is no more satisfied in the interval cd, and the oscillation of order 2/3 is excited, thus disturbing the continuation of the original subharmonic oscillation.

As mentioned above, the curves in Fig. 12.7 are drawn for the case of $c_1 = 0$ and $c_5 = 1$. With increasing c_1 (or decreasing c_5), however, these curves move towards the point $(1, 0)$, as we see from the expressions for the θ's in equations (12.22). Hence, as the departure from linearity is reduced, the interval cd in the second unstable region contracts and finally disappears. We also sees that in no case the parameters $\theta_3 \sim \theta_6$ enter into their respective unstable regions. Hence, in the end, it may be concluded that the stability conditions for $n = 2$ as well as for $n = 1$ must be considered in the case when the non-linearity is character-ized by a quintic function. The points $A \sim D$ in Fig. 12.6 correspond, respec-tively, to the critical points $a \sim d$ in Fig. 12.7, so that the subharmonic oscillation of order 1/3 is maintained in the stable state only in the intervals AC and BD.

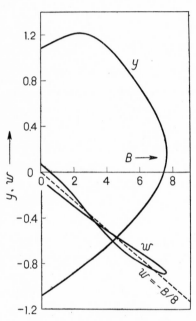

We shall now discuss the approximation in the foregoing analysis just as we did at the end of the preceding section. Let the differential equation be given by

$$\frac{d^2 v}{d\tau^2} + v^5 = B \cos 3\tau .$$

Substituting the periodic solution

$$v = y \cos \tau + w \cos 3\tau ,$$

and equating the coefficients of $\cos \tau$ and $\cos 3\tau$ separately to zero, we obtain

$$\left. \begin{array}{l} y^4 + \dfrac{5}{2} y^3 w + 6 y^2 w^2 + 3 y w^3 + 3 w^4 - \dfrac{8}{5} = 0 , \\[2mm] \dfrac{5}{16} y^5 + \dfrac{15}{8} y^4 w + \dfrac{15}{8} y^3 w^2 + \dfrac{15}{4} y^2 w^3 + \dfrac{5}{8} w^5 \\[2mm] \hspace{5cm} -9w = B . \end{array} \right\}$$

$$(12.24)$$

Fɪɢ. 12.8. Relationship between y, w and B in (12.24).

Figure 12.8 is obtained by plotting (12.24). Thus we see that the approximation $w = -B/8$ may also be applied without serious error.

For $B = 0$ and $B = \text{max.}$, the values of y, w and the parameters $\theta_0 \sim \theta_3$ in equations (12.22) are calculated and shown in Table 12.2.

Tᴀʙʟᴇ 12.2.†   Values of y, w and the θ's for $B = 0$ and $B = \text{max.}$

B	y	w	θ_0	θ_1	θ_2	θ_3
0	1.0759	0.0716	2.7795	2.0327	0.7655	0.1337
Max. = 7.546	0.1542	−0.8818	1.2651	−0.3385	−0.3736	0.8210

† For the case in which the non-linear characteristic is given by a quintic function.

Substituting the values of θ_1 into equation (12.18), we have

$$\theta_0 = 3.0327 \quad \text{for} \quad B = 0 \,, \quad \left.\begin{array}{c} \\ \\ \end{array}\right\}$$
$$\theta_0 = 1.3385 \quad \text{for} \quad B = \text{max.}$$

These values differ from those given in Table 12.2 by 9.1 percent and 5.8 percent respectively. Applying again the closer approximation (12.19) instead of (12.18), we obtain

$$\theta_0 = 2.7234 \quad \text{for} \quad B = 0 \,, \quad \left.\begin{array}{c} \\ \\ \end{array}\right\}$$
$$\theta_0 = 1.2415 \quad \text{for} \quad B = \text{max.}$$

The discrepancies are reduced down to 1.9 percent and 2.0 percent respectively, and we may conclude that the stability limits of the first unstable region are given by the condition that the external force B has its limiting values.

We have so far discussed the stability limits of the first unstable region. A similar investigation may be carried out for the second unstable region. But the stability limits have no particular relation to the external force in this case, and besides, as we shall see in a later experiment, the small parasitic oscillation of order 2/3 can exist along with the original subharmonic oscillation in the neighborhood of the stability limits, so that the points c, d in Fig. 12.7, however accurately they might be determined, would not represent the exact critical points at which the original subharmonic oscillation ceases. Therefore a further investigation into the stability limits of the second unstable region is not important and is omitted here.

12.3. Experimental investigation [8, 12]

In this section we shall compare the theoretical results (in the preceding sections) with experiments conducted for an electrical oscillatory circuit containing a saturable iron-core inductance and a capacitance in series. As mentioned previously in Section 6, the circuit equation has the form of (10.1) when an alternating voltage (60 c.p.s. in our case) is applied to the circuit. When an appropriate initial condition is prescribed, the subharmonic oscillation of order 1/3, i.e., of 20 c.p.s., may easily be started in the circuit.

Now, making use of a transformer-core inductance as the non-linear element, we first determine the region in which the subharmonic oscillation of order 1/3 is sustained. In Fig. 12.9a this region is depicted by hatched lines. The appearance of the blank part inside the sustaining region is an arresting feature and was previously reported by the present author [8] and others [23]. But no theoretical consideration was given at that time.

From the preceding analysis, however, it will be deduced that the blank part mentioned above corresponds to the unstable regions of order $n \geq 2$, because

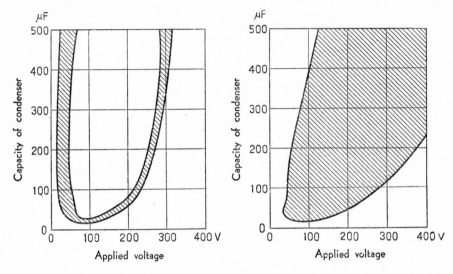

(a) Magnetization curve by (12.25).   (b) Magnetization curve by (12.26).

Fig. 12.9.   Regions in which the 1/3-harmonic oscillation is sustained.

the non-linear characteristic of the ordinary transformer core is expressed by

$$f(v) = c_1 v + c_3 v^3 + c_5 v^5 + c_7 v^7 + \cdots,^* \qquad (12.25)$$

in which the coefficients c_5, c_7, $\cdots$ predominate c_1, c_3. If we use a core whose characteristic is expressed by

$$f(v) = c_1 v + c_3 v^3, \qquad (12.26)$$

the blank part inside the sustaining region will be eliminated. Such a core is not available in practice, but we can obtain the characteristic (12.26) by connecting a number of inductance coils in series and adjusting the length of the air-gap which is interposed in each core. Figure 12.10 shows an example in which two cores are used, one with air-gap and the other without. The resultant characteristic shows a fairly good approximation to equation (12.26). By making

---

* Physically, equation (12.25) represents the magnetization curve of the core, i. e., the relationship between the magnetic flux v and the magnetizing current $f(v)$.

use of this composite inductance, the sustaining region of the subharmonic oscillation of order 1/3 is determined and plotted in Fig. 12.9b. We see that the unstable oscillations corresponding to the unstable regions of order $n \geq 2$ are completely excluded, and so the experimental verification is quite satisfactory.

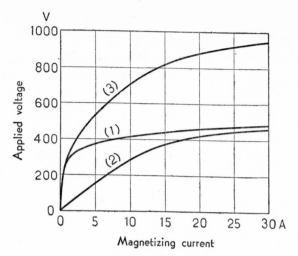

FIG. 12.10. Combined characteristic approximated to a cubic curve; (1) without air-gap, (2) with air-gap, (3) combined characteristic of (1) and (2).

We further measure the harmonic content in these oscillations with a heterodyne harmonic analyzer. Figure 12.11 shows the result for the cases in which the non-linearities are given by equations (12.25) and (12.26) respectively. In Fig. 12.11a, we observe the higher harmonics of orders 2/3, 5/3, 7/3, ⋯, among which the

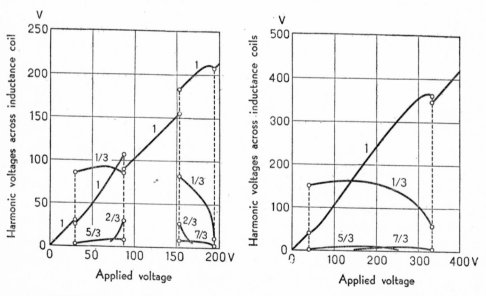

(a) Magnetization curve by (12.25). (b) Magnetization curve by (12.26).

FIG. 12.11. Harmonic analysis of oscillations.

oscillation of order 2/3 is significant, because it is this oscillation (related to the second unstable region) that grows up rapidly and interrupts the original subharmonic oscillation (see Figs. 12.7 and 12.9 a). Whereas, in Fig. 12.11 b, no such obstructive oscillation is observed, and the subharmonic oscillation of order 1/3 is sustained in the whole region (see Figs. 12.2 and 12.9 b).

Finally it is added that the subharmonic oscillation of order 1/5 can occur when the non-linearity is given by equation (12.25), but this oscillation is by no means observed when the non-linearity is given by equation (12.26). These results also agree with the investigation in Section 11.

13.1. Subharmonic oscillation of order 1/2

(a) Fundamental equation

This section deals with the subharmonic oscillation of order 1/2, whose least period is twice the period of the external force. As already mentioned in Section 11, the oscillation of order 1/2 is liable to occur when the non-linearity is unsymmetrical, and so we consider the differential equation

$$\frac{d^2v}{d\tau^2}+k\frac{dv}{d\tau}+c_1v+c_2v^2+c_3v^3 = B\cos 2\tau\,,\qquad(13.1)$$

in which the non-linear restoring force is made unsymmetrical by the presence of c_2v^2. Similar to the case in Section 7.1, this equation is readily transformed to the alternative form

$$\frac{d^2v'}{d\tau^2}+k\frac{dv'}{d\tau}+c_1'v'+c_3'v'^3 = B\cos 2\tau+B_0\,,\qquad(13.2)$$

in which the restoring force is symmetrical, but the external force is rendered unsymmetrical since it contains the unidirectional component B_0. For the convenience of analysis, we shall hereafter take the form (13.2), and investigate the subharmonic oscillation of order 1/2 in the following.

(b) Periodic states of equilibrium

Putting, in particular, $c_1'=0$ and $c_3'=1$ in equation (13.2), thereby not loosing the non-linearity, we consider the differential equation

$$\frac{d^2v}{d\tau^2}+k\frac{dv}{d\tau}+v^3 = B\cos 2\tau+B_0\,.\qquad(13.3)$$

Now, the periodic solution may be assumed in the form

$$v(\tau) = v_0+x\sin\tau+y\cos\tau+w\cos 2\tau\,,\qquad(13.4)$$

where only the constant term v_0, the subharmonic oscillation $x \sin \tau + y \cos \tau$, and the component with impressed frequency $w \cos 2\tau$ are considered for their prime importance. Following Mandelstam and Papalexi [21, p. 227], the amplitude w is approximated by

$$w = -\frac{1}{3} B \qquad \text{[see equation (11.4)]} . \qquad (13.5)$$

This approximation is valid as long as the non-linearity is small, but, as will be evinced later, it can still be applied without serious error in the case when the departure from linearity is large.

Substituting (13.4) into (13.3) and equating the constant term and the coefficients of $\sin \tau$ and $\cos \tau$ on both sides respectively, we have

$$\left. \begin{aligned} V_0(v_0, x, y) &= v_0^3 + \frac{3}{2} v_0 r^2 + \frac{3}{2} v_0 w^2 + \frac{3}{4}(y^2 - x^2) w = B_0 , \\[2mm] X(v_0, x, y) &= -x - ky + 3v_0^2 x + \frac{3}{4} r^2 x + \frac{3}{2} x w^2 - 3v_0 x w = 0 , \\[2mm] Y(v_0, x, y) &= -y + kx + 3v_0^2 y + \frac{3}{4} r^2 y + \frac{3}{2} y w^2 + 3v_0 y w = 0 . \end{aligned} \right\} \qquad (13.6)$$

The second and the third equations of (13.6) may also be written as

$$\left. \begin{aligned} Ax + ky &= -3v_0 xw , \\[1mm] Ay - kx &= 3v_0 yw , \end{aligned} \right\}$$

where
$$\qquad (13.7)$$
$$A = 1 - \left(3v_0^2 + \frac{3}{4} r^2 + \frac{3}{2} w^2 \right), \quad r^2 = x^2 + y^2 .$$

Since w is fixed by (13.5), we can determine v_0, x and y in the periodic solution (13.4) by solving the simultaneous equations (13.6) for given values of B and B_0. An example of the calculated results is drawn in Fig. 13.1 for $k = 0.2$, showing the relationship between B_0 and r for several values of B.

(c) Stability condition of the periodic solutions

Let the variation from the equilibrium states be denoted by ξ. Then, putting $v(\tau) + \xi$ for $v(\tau)$ in equation (13.3), we obtain the following variational equation, i. e.,

$$\frac{d^2\xi}{d\tau^2} + k \frac{d\xi}{d\tau} + 3v^2\xi = 0 . \qquad (13.8)$$

Eliminating the second term by the transformation

$$\xi = e^{-\delta\tau}\cdot\eta\,, \quad \text{with} \quad \delta = k/2\,, \tag{13.9}$$

equation (13.8) leads to

$$\frac{d^2\eta}{d\tau^2}+(-\delta^2+3v^2)\,\eta = 0\,. \tag{13.10}$$

Since the periodic solution $v(\tau)$ was determined in the preceding paragraph, sub-

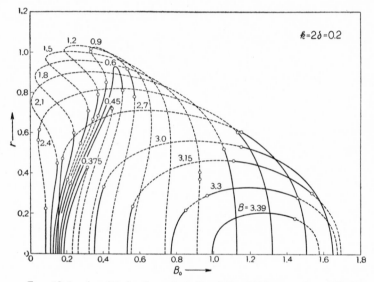

Fɪɢ. 13.1. Amplitude characteristic of the 1/2-harmonic oscillation.

stitution of (13.4) into (13.10) leads to the linear equation of Hill's type, namely,

$$\frac{d^2\eta}{d\tau^2}+\Big[\theta_0+2\sum_{\nu=1}^{4}\theta_\nu\cos\,(\nu\tau-\varepsilon_\nu)\Big]\eta = 0\,,$$

where

$$\theta_0 = \frac{3}{2}\,(2v_0^2+x^2+y^2+w^2)-\delta^2\,,$$

$$\theta_\nu^2 = \theta_{\nu s}^2+\theta_{\nu c}^2\,, \qquad\qquad \varepsilon_\nu = \arctan\frac{\theta_{\nu s}}{\theta_{\nu c}}\,,$$

$$\theta_{1s} = 3x\left(v_0-\frac{1}{2}\,w\right)\,, \qquad \theta_{1c} = 3y\left(v_0+\frac{1}{2}\,w\right)\,,$$

$$\theta_{2s} = \frac{3}{2}\,xy\,, \qquad\qquad \theta_{2c} = \frac{3}{4}\,(4v_0w-x^2+y^2)\,,$$

$$\theta_{3s} = \frac{3}{2}\,xw\,, \qquad\qquad \theta_{3c} = \frac{3}{2}\,yw\,,$$

$$\theta_{4s} = 0\,, \qquad\qquad \theta_{4c} = \frac{3}{4}\,w^2\,.$$

$$\left.\rule{0pt}{9em}\right\} \tag{13.11}$$

Following the investigation in Section 5.1, the equilibrium states will be stable provided that

$$\left[\theta_0-\left(\frac{n}{2}\right)^2\right]^2+2\left[\theta_0+\left(\frac{n}{2}\right)^2\right]\delta^2+\delta^4>\theta_n^2, \qquad n=1,\ 2,\ 3,\ \cdots. \qquad (13.12)$$

This is the stability condition (of the first approximation) for the nth unstable region, and thus, in order that the periodic state of equilibrium be stable, the condition (13.12) must be satisfied for all values of n simultaneously.*

From (13.11) the values of $\theta_0 \sim \theta_4$ may be calculated for given B and B_0,

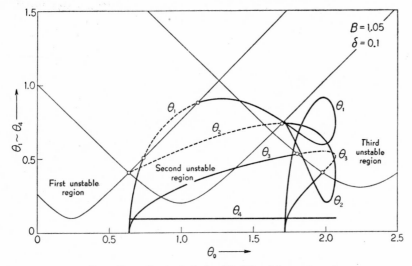

Fig. 13.2. Loci of θ's in (13.11) with varying B_0.

since the equilibrium state (13.4) is already determined in the preceding paragraph. In Fig. 13.2 the loci of $\theta_1 \sim \theta_4$ are shown with varying B_0 for $\delta=0.1$ and $B=1.05$, while the unstable regions in this plane are readily obtained by (13.12). The boundaries between the stable and the unstable regions are shown by hyperbolic curves, the upper sides of which are the unstable regions. Hence, the loci of $\theta_1 \sim \theta_3$ enter into their unstable regions in the dotted-line intervals respectively, and the corresponding equilibrium states are unstable.

Thus far the discussion of stability refers to the first approximation as given by equation (13.12). The analytical result obtained in this manner, however, does not satisfactorily agree with the experiments in the following section. Particularly in the case when $n=2$, this condition fails to verify that

---

* Generally, if θ_n enters into the nth unstable region, the $n/2$th harmonic of the subharmonic oscillation, i. e. the oscillation of order $n/4$ is excited with negative damping.

the vertical tangency of the characteristic curves of Fig. 13.1 takes place at the stability limit of the second unstable region. This is due to the deficiency of approximation in deriving the condition (13.12). However, this particular condition for $n = 2$ is most important, because it ascertains the stability against building up of the unstable oscillation having the same frequency as that of the subharmonic. Therefore, it will be preferable to resort to the improved stability condition (5.13) instead of (5.7). Thus we put $n = 2$ in (5.13) and write

$$\left.\begin{array}{l} 4\,(\delta^2 - \mu^2) = (\theta_0 + \delta^2 - 1)^2 - \theta_2^2 - 2\,\dfrac{\theta_0 + \delta^2 - 1}{\theta_0 + \delta^2}\,\theta_1^2 \\[2ex] \qquad + \dfrac{2}{\theta_0 + \delta^2}\,[\theta_{2c}\,(\theta_{1c}^2 - \theta_{1s}^2) + 2\theta_{2s}\theta_{1c}\theta_{1s}] + 4\delta^2 > 0\,.^* \end{array}\right\} \quad (13.13)$$

Substituting the parameters given by (13.11), we obtain

$$\left.\begin{array}{l} -\dfrac{3}{4}\,Ar^2 + \dfrac{1}{3\left(v_0^2 + \dfrac{1}{2}\,r^2 + \dfrac{1}{2}\,w^2\right)}\left[\dfrac{3}{2}\,r^2\left(1 + 3v_0^2 - \dfrac{3}{2}\,r^2 - \dfrac{3}{2}\,w^2\right)\left(A + \dfrac{3}{2}\,w^2\right)\right. \\[3ex] \qquad\qquad \left. + \dfrac{9}{8}\,Ar^4 + \dfrac{3}{16}\,\dfrac{A^2r^4}{v_0^2}\right] > 0\,. \end{array}\right\} \quad (13.14)$$

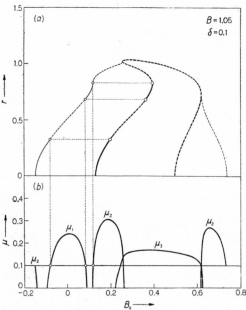

Fig. 13.3. Stability of equilibrium states.
a. Amplitude of subharmonic oscillation.
b. Characteristic exponent related to it.

Further, proceeding just as in Section 5.3 (d), this stability condition leads to

$$v_0\left(1 - 3v_0^2 - \dfrac{3}{4}\,r^2\right)\dfrac{dB_0}{dr^2} > 0\,, \quad (13.15)$$

where we have considered the case when B_0 varies while B is held constant. Hence it is clear that the characteristic curves of Fig. 13.1 have vertical tangents at the stability limit $dB_0/dr^2 = 0$.

Now, taking again the case of $\delta = 0.1$ and $B = 1.05$, we show in Fig. 13.3a the amplitude r of the subharmonic oscillation against B_0. The curve is extended on both sides by fine

---

* Referring to Section 5.3 (d), it is readily verified that this condition leads to the form of equation (5.32) in which V_0, X, and Y are given by (13.6).

lines so as to obtain a single value of r for a given B_0. The value of μ_2 (the suffix designating the order of the unstable region) is calculated by (13.13), i.e.,

$$\left.\begin{aligned}
4\mu_2^2 &= -(\theta_0+\delta^2-1)^2+\theta_2^2+2\,\frac{\theta_0+\delta^2-1}{\theta_0+\delta^2}\,\theta_1^2 \\
&\quad -\frac{2}{\theta_0+\delta^2}\,[\theta_{2c}\,(\theta_{1c}^2-\theta_{1s}^2)+2\theta_{2s}\theta_{1c}\theta_{1s}]\,,\dagger
\end{aligned}\right\} \qquad (13.16)$$

and is plotted against B_0 in Fig. 13.3 b. The curves of μ_1 and μ_3 calculated from

$$\mu_n^2 = -\left[\theta_0+\left(\frac{n}{2}\right)^2\right]+\sqrt{n^2\theta_0+\theta_n^2}\,, \qquad \text{[see equation (4.14)]} \qquad (13.17)$$

are also shown in this figure.‡ Since the equilibrium states are stable in the case when $|\mu_n| < \delta$ ($= 0.1$), the stable states are readily determined and marked by full lines in Fig. 13.3a.

Carrying out similar calculations for various values of B, the stable states of equilibrium are determined and marked by full lines in Fig. 13.1. Further, in Fig. 13.4, this result is rewritten in the B, B_0-plane so as to show the region in which the subharmonic oscillation of order 1/2 is sustained in the stable state. Finally the complete amplitude characteristics of the subharmonic oscillation are shown in Fig. 13.5 in which the stable states are depicted by full lines.

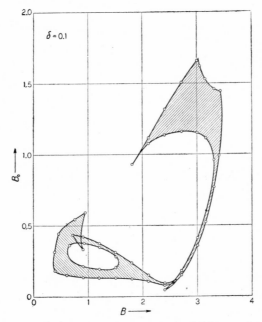

FIG. 13.4. Region in which the 1/2-harmonic oscillation is sustained (calculated).

---

† As noticed in Section 5.2 (a), equation (13.16) is valid only when $|\mu_2| = \delta$, and therefore it may not give a correct value of μ_2 when $|\mu_2| \neq \delta$. However, it does not matter when we discuss the stability problem only.

‡ In Fig. 13.3b we see that the curves of μ_2 and μ_3 intersect, and so real values of μ_2 and μ_3 exist simultaneously for certain values of B_0. This is due to the deficiency of approximation in computing the characteristic exponent, and, properly speaking, these curves should not intersect, for, if they do, it leads to the contradiction that there are four linearly independent solutions for a given second order differential equation.

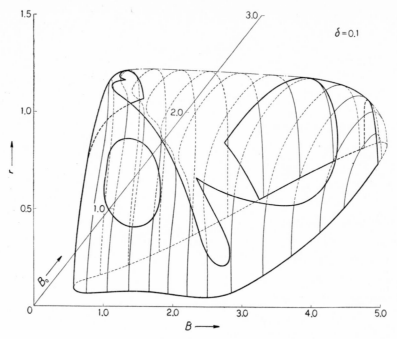

Fɪɢ. 13.5. Complete amplitude characteristic of the 1/2-harmonic
oscillation (calculated).

(d) On the approximation of equation (13.5)

As we have previously mentioned in Sections 12.1 (c) and 12.2, the relation

$$w = \frac{1}{1-\nu^2} B = -\frac{1}{8} B, \quad \text{for} \quad \nu = 3$$

is a fairly good approximation even when the departure from linearity is large. This is also the case when we deal with the subharmonic oscillation of order 1/2 (*viz.*, $\nu = 2$).* We shall verify this for the non-dissipative case, and assume the periodic solution of the form

$$v = v_0 + y \cos \tau + w \cos 2\tau \qquad (13.18)$$

where v_0, y, and w are unknown quantities to be determined shortly.

Substituting (13.18) into the original equation (13.3), therein putting $k = 0$, and equating the constant term, the coefficients of $\cos \tau$ and $\cos 2\tau$ on both sides respectively, we obtain

---

* In equation (13.3) we considered the case when $c_1' = 0$ and $c_3' = 1$.

$$v_0^3 + \frac{3}{2} v_0 y^2 + \frac{3}{2} v_0 w^2 + \frac{3}{4} y^2 w = B_0 \,,$$

$$3v_0^2 + 3v_0 w + \frac{3}{4} y^2 + \frac{3}{2} w^2 - 1 = 0 \,,$$

$$3v_0^2 w + \frac{3}{2} v_0 y^2 + \frac{3}{2} y^2 w + \frac{3}{4} w^3 - 4w = B \,.$$

$$\left. \right\} \quad (13.19)$$

The coefficients v_0, y, and w in (13.18) may be determined by solving (13.19) for given values of B and B_0.

Upon carrying out the calculation, it will be seen that the approximation (13.5) may be applied without serious error. Taking the case of $B_0 = 0.3$ by way of example, the values of v_0, y, and w are plotted against B in Fig. 13.6. It is apparent that the exact values of w obtained from (13.19) are closely approximated by $w = -B/3$.

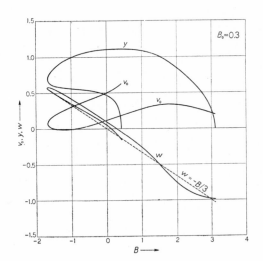

Fig. 13.6. Relationship between v_0, y, w and B in (13.19).

13.2. Experimental investigation

In this section we shall observe the subharmonic oscillation of order 1/2 governed by the original equation (13.2) or (13.3), and compare the results obtained from experiment with those of the foregoing analysis.

The schematic diagram illustrated in Fig. 13.7 shows an electrical circuit in which the subharmonic oscillation takes place due to the saturable-core inductance L under the action of the alternating voltage $E \sin 2\omega t$. As shown in the figure, the secondary winding is provided on the core in order to afford the unsymmetry to the non-linear characteristic by forcing a constant direct-current flow through it. With the notations of Fig. 13.7, we have

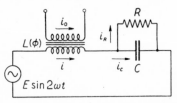

Fig. 13.7. Oscillatory circuit containing reactor with d-c superimposed.

$$n \frac{d\phi}{dt} + Ri_R = E \sin 2\omega t \,,$$

$$Ri_R = \frac{1}{C} \int i_C dt \,,$$

$$i = i_R + i_C \,,$$

$$\left. \right\} \quad (13.20)$$

where n is the number of turns of the primary winding and ϕ the magnetic flux in the core.

Proceeding in the same manner as in Section 6, we introduce the non-dimensional variable u, u_0, and v in place of i, i_0, and ϕ by the relations

$$i = I_n \cdot u, \quad i_0 = I_n \cdot u_0, \quad \text{and} \quad \phi = \mathit{\Phi}_n \cdot v, \tag{13.21}$$

where I_n and $\mathit{\Phi}_n$ are appropriate unit quantities of the current and flux respectively. Then, neglecting hysteresis, we may take the saturation curve of the form*

$$u + u_0 = c_1 v + c_3 v^3 + c_5 v^5 + \cdots, \tag{13.22}$$

where c_1, c_3, c_5, $\cdots$ are constants characteristic of the core. Further, as we have done previously, the units I_n and $\mathit{\Phi}_n$ may expediently be fixed by

$$\left. \begin{array}{l} n\omega^2 C \mathit{\Phi}_n = I_n, \\[2mm] c_1 + c_3 + c_5 + \cdots = 1. \end{array} \right\} \tag{13.23}$$

Then, eliminating i_R and i_C from equations (13.20) and making use of (13.21), (13.22), and (13.23), we obtain

where

$$\left. \begin{array}{c} \dfrac{d^2v}{d\tau^2} + k\dfrac{dv}{d\tau} + c_1 v + c_3 v^3 + c_5 v^5 + \cdots = B\cos 2\tau + B_0, \\[4mm] \tau = \omega t - \dfrac{1}{2}\arctan\dfrac{k}{2}, \quad k = \dfrac{1}{\omega CR}, \\[4mm] B = \dfrac{E}{n\omega\mathit{\Phi}_n}\sqrt{4+k^2}, \quad B_0 = u_0. \end{array} \right\} \tag{13.24}$$

Further, in order to secure a better agreement with the foregoing analysis, we use a composite reactor† whose saturation curve is given by the following cubic in v, i.e.,

$$u + u_0 = v^3.$$

Then the first equation of (13.24) leads to the original form (13.3).

We now proceed to describe the result of experiments which are effective in verifying the foregoing analysis. We first determine the region in which

---

* It is tacitly assumed that the secondary winding of the reactor has the same number of turns as that of the primary winding.

† As already explained in Section 12.3, a number of magnetic cores with air-gaps of appropriate length are used to obtain the desired saturation curve.

the subharmonic oscillation of order 1/2 is sustained in stable states. This region is plotted in the V_{ac}, I_{dc}-plane of Fig. 13.8 where V_{ac} is the applied a-c voltage and I_{dc} the constant direct-current in the secondary winding (see Fig. 13.7). Since the coordinates V_{ac} and I_{dc} correspond, respectively, to B and B_0 in the preceding section, a considerable agreement is found between Figs. 13.4 and 13.8.‡ In Fig. 13.8 we see that the region of the 1/2-harmonic oscillation may be divided into two domains as indicated by changing the direction of the hatched lines. For convenience sake, we shall distinguish them

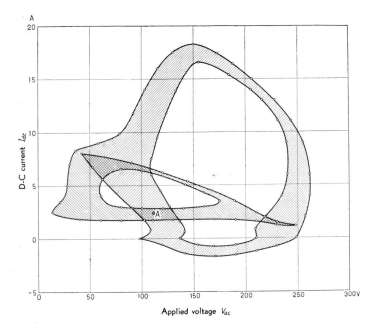

Fɪɢ. 13.8. Region in which the 1/2-harmonic oscillation is sustained (experimental).

as the first and the second domains, the former being extended between $I_{dc} \simeq 2 \sim 8$ amp., and the latter between $I_{dc} \simeq -2 \sim 18$ amp. In the particular domains common to these (e.g., at point A), two kinds of 1/2-harmonic oscillation exist for a given set of V_{ac} and I_{dc}. The wave form of these oscillations will be shown shortly.

As expected from the result of Fig. 13.3, the blank part inside the first domain is due to the self-excitation of the unstable oscillation of order 1/4,

‡ It was theoretically verified that the region of the 1/2-harmonic oscillation in Fig. 13.4 extends down to the negative side of B_0 in the case when the damping coefficient k (or δ) was sufficiently small.

because in this case the characteristic exponent μ_1 associated with the first unstable region of Hill's equation grows up and the stability condition $|\mu_1| < \delta$ fails. Similarly, in the blank part surrounded by the second domain, the unstable oscillation of order 3/4 disturbs the original 1/2-harmonic oscillation, because $|\mu_3|$ is greater than δ in this case.

The above discussion is confirmed experimentally by observing the wave form of the 1/2-harmonic oscillation. Oscillograms (a) and (c) in Fig. 13.9 are

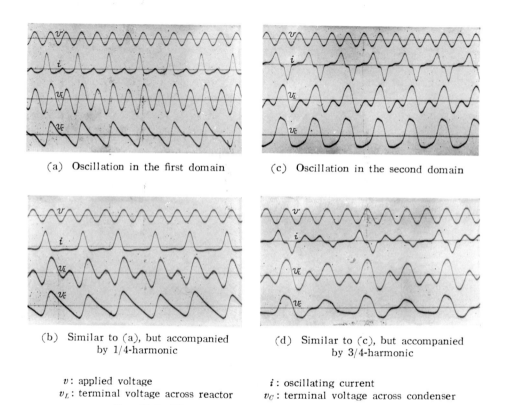

(a)   Oscillation in the first domain   (c)   Oscillation in the second domain

(b)   Similar to (a), but accompanied   (d)   Similar to (c), but accompanied
      by 1/4-harmonic   by 3/4-harmonic

v : applied voltage i : oscillating current
v_L : terminal voltage across reactor v_C : terminal voltage across condenser

Fig. 13.9. Wave forms of the 1/2-harmonic oscillation.

obtained in the case when the values of V_{ac} and I_{ac} are given by the coordinates of the point A in Fig. 13.8, (a) being associated with the first domain, and (c) with the second domain. Oscillograms (b) and (d) are obtained in the cases when A approaches the blank parts of the first and the second domains respectively. The voltage v_L across the reactor is analyzed by making use of a harmonic analyzer. The result is shown in Fig. 13.10 in which (a)~(d) correspond to Oscillograms (a)~(d) in Fig. 13.9. Thus, as expected, the oscillation of order 1/4 is detected in (b), and the oscillation of order 3/4 is noticeable in (d).*

We further measure the harmonic voltages across the reactor with varying V_{ac} while holding I_{dc} at a constant value (4 amp.), and obtain Fig. 13.11. It is evidently shown therein that the building up of the unstable oscillations of orders 1/4 and 3/4 causes the collapse of the 1/2-harmonic oscillation in the blank parts of the first and the second domains respectively.

Finally the complete amplitude characteristic of the 1/2-harmonic oscillation measured with the harmonic analyzer is plotted in Fig. 13.12, showing a satisfactory agreement with the theoretical result obtained in Fig. 13.5.

In conclusion, comparing the experimental results with the preceding analysis, the salient features of the 1/2-harmonic oscillation are summed up as follows.

---

* It is noticed that, in (a) and (c) of Fig. 13.10, the oscillations of orders 1/2 and 1 predominate over all others. Since the reactor voltage is proportional to the time-derivative of the flux in the core, the approximation given by equation (13.4) to the periodic solution of the flux is quite satisfactory.

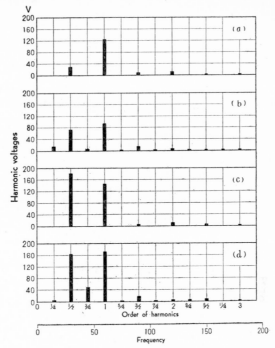

FIG. 13.10. Harmonic analysis of v_L in the oscillograms of Fig. 13.9.

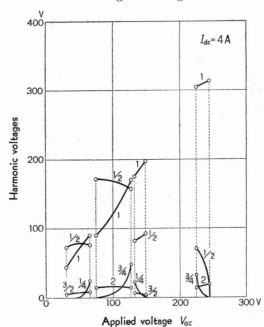

FIG. 13.11. Harmonic analysis of voltage across the reactor.

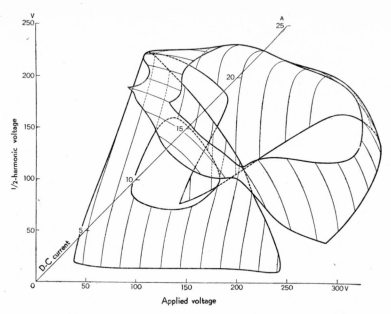

Fɪɢ. 13.12. Complete amplitude characteristic of the 1/2-harmonic
oscillation (experimental).

(a) The 1/2-harmonic oscillation is liable to occur in the case when either the non-linear restoring force or the impressed force is unsymmetrical. It is, however, to be mentioned that the oscillation may still take place when the system is symmetrical, because, as long as the damping of the system is sufficiently small, the 1/2-harmonic oscillation occurs even when $B_0 = 0$ in Fig. 13.4 or $I_{dc} = 0$ in Fig. 13.8.

(b) Contrary to the result obtained for the 1/3-harmonic oscillation, two different kinds of 1/2-harmonic oscillation may be sustained under certain circumstances in the same system but with different initial conditions (see the overlapped domains in Figs. 13.4 and 13.8).

(c) The 1/2-harmonic oscillation is frequently accompanied by the self-excitation of the unstable oscillation of order 1/4 or 3/4 which will no longer permit the continuation of the original oscillation. The generalized stability condition given in Chapter I is effective in detecting this instability.

PART II

NON-LINEAR OSCILLATIONS IN TRANSIENT STATES

CHAPTER V

HARMONIC OSCILLATIONS

14. Introduction

It was first mentioned in Section 1 that various types of periodic solution may exist for a given non-linear differential equation, and that which one of them will take place depends on the initial conditions. In Part I we have concentrated our attention on the periodic solutions and discussed the problem of their stability. We are now to investigate the transient state which shows the oscillations until they get to the steady state. When this is done, the relationship between the initial conditions and the resulting periodic oscillations will be made clear. But, it is hardly possible to solve the non-linear differential equation with an arbitrary initial condition, as we usually do for the linear type of equation. Fortunately, however, we have, to some extent, succeeded in investigating the transient state of oscillations by means of the geometrical (or topological) method of analysis [9, 10].

Thus, the method of solution used in the following sections is first to transform the differential equation (under certain restrictions) to the form

$$\frac{dy}{dx} = \frac{Y(x, y)}{X(x, y)}, \qquad (14.1)$$

and then to find its integral curves with the basic idea that the singular points of equation (14.1) are correlated with the steady state of oscillations, and the integral curves with the transient state.

With this method of investigation we shall first study the harmonic oscillations in the present chapter, and then the subharmonic oscillations in Chapter VI.

15. Periodic solutions and their stability

Although we have dealt with this problem in Section 6, we shall review it with concern in the transient state, rather than confine attention to the steady state.

Now, we consider the fundamental equation

$$\frac{d^2v}{d\tau^2} + k\frac{dv}{d\tau} + v^3 = B\cos\tau,\tag{15.1}$$

where the non-linear restoring force is expressed by a cubic function in v. In the case of harmonic oscillations in which the fundamental component having the period 2π predominates over the higher harmonics, this equation admits a solution of the form

$$v(\tau) = x(\tau)\sin\tau + y(\tau)\cos\tau,\tag{15.2}$$

where the amplitudes $x(\tau)$ and $y(\tau)$ are both functions of τ, but are ultimately reduced to constants after the transient state has elapsed.*

Substituting (15.2) into (15.1) and equating the terms containing $\sin\tau$ and $\cos\tau$ separately to zero, we obtain

$$\left.\begin{aligned}
\frac{dx}{d\tau} &= \frac{1}{2}\left[B - kx + y - \frac{3}{4}r^2y\right] \equiv X(x,\,y),\\[2mm]
\frac{dy}{d\tau} &= \frac{1}{2}\left[-x - ky + \frac{3}{4}r^2x\right] \equiv Y(x,\,y),
\end{aligned}\right\}\tag{15.3}$$

where

$$r^2 = x^2 + y^2.$$

However, we have here to set forth the following restrictions in deriving equations (15.3).

(1) The amplitudes $x(\tau)$, $y(\tau)$ are functions of τ, but only slowly variable, *viz.*,

$$\frac{dx}{d\tau} \ll x,\qquad \frac{dy}{d\tau} \ll y,$$

$$\frac{d^2x}{d\tau^2} \ll \frac{dx}{d\tau},\qquad \frac{d^2y}{d\tau^2} \ll \frac{dy}{d\tau},$$

so that the terms containing $d^2x/d\tau^2$ and $d^2y/d\tau^2$ may be neglected.

(2) The damping coefficient k is a comparatively small quantity.

The results derived from equations (15.3) may therefore not be applicable to the case in which the higher harmonic oscillations are noticeable. But as

---

* See equation (6.7) in Section 6.

far as we deal with the harmonic oscillations, equations (15.3) may be considered to be legitimate. †

Equations (15.3) play a significant role in our following investigation, since they serve as the fundamental relations in studying the transient state as well as the steady state. We shall, for the time being, consider the steady state in which the amplitudes $x(\tau)$, $y(\tau)$, in equation (15.2) are constant, i.e.,

$$
\left.
\begin{aligned}
dx/d\tau = X(x,\ y) = 0\,, \\
dy/d\tau = Y(x,\ y) = 0\,.
\end{aligned}
\right\} \tag{15.4}
$$

From (15.3) and (15.4) the amplitude r_0 of the periodic solution $v(\tau)$ is given by

$$
B^2 = r_0^2 (A^2 + k^2)\,,
$$

where

$$
A = \frac{3}{4}\, r_0^2 - 1\,, \tag{15.5}
$$

and the components x_0, y_0 of the amplitude r_0 are found to be

$$
Bx_0 = kr_0^2\,, \qquad Ax_0 = ky_0\,,
$$

or

$$
x_0^2 = \frac{r_0^2}{1 + \left(\dfrac{A}{k}\right)^2}\,, \qquad y_0^2 = \frac{r_0^2}{1 + \left(\dfrac{k}{A}\right)^2}\,. \tag{15.6}
$$

These results agree with the investigation in Section 6 (b).

We have already discussed the stability of the periodic solution in Section 6 (c). If, in particular, we consider the stability condition for the first unstable region only [*viz.*, $n = 1$ in equation (5.5)], it may also be obtained by the use of Hurwitz's criterion [see Section 5.3 (a)], and so, bearing this in mind, we shall reconsider the stability condition (6.11) or (6.12).

To effect this, we consider small variations ξ and η from the amplitudes x_0 and y_0 as given by equation (15.6), and determine whether these deviations approach zero or not with increase of the time τ. From equations (15.3) we have

---

† The following discussion is based on equations (15.3), and so the results which will be obtained from them are valid as long as these equations are correctly applied. Strictly speaking, therefore, the assumption (originally due to Appleton and van der Pol [2, 28]) which is used to derive the autonomous system (15.3) should be examined in order to expect a correct description of the oscillations governed by equation (15.1). Some attempts in this line have been done by Kryloff and Bogoliuboff [40, p. 28] and Lefschetz [38, p. 341] in the case when the non-linearity is sufficiently small.

$$\frac{d\xi}{d\tau} = \frac{\partial X}{\partial x}\,\xi + \frac{\partial X}{\partial y}\,\eta \,,$$

and

$$\frac{d\eta}{d\tau} = \frac{\partial Y}{\partial x}\,\xi + \frac{\partial Y}{\partial y}\,\eta \,.$$

(15.7)

The solutions of these simultaneous equations have the form $e^{\lambda\tau}$, where λ is determined by

$$\begin{vmatrix} \dfrac{\partial X}{\partial x} - \lambda & \dfrac{\partial X}{\partial y} \\[2ex] \dfrac{\partial Y}{\partial x} & \dfrac{\partial Y}{\partial y} - \lambda \end{vmatrix} = 0 \,.$$

(15.8)

The variations ξ and η approach zero with the time τ, provided that the real part of λ is negative, and the corresponding periodic solution determined from (15.2) and (15.6) is stable. This stability condition is given by Hurwitz's criterion [14] as

$$-\frac{\partial X}{\partial x} - \frac{\partial Y}{\partial y} > 0 \,,$$

and

$$\frac{\partial X}{\partial x}\,\frac{\partial Y}{\partial y} - \frac{\partial Y}{\partial x}\,\frac{\partial X}{\partial y} > 0 \,.$$

(15.9)

Substituting (15.3) and (15.5) into (15.9), we obtain

$$k > 0 \,,$$

and

$$\frac{27}{16}\,r_0^4 - 3r_0^2 + k^2 + 1 > 0 \,, \quad \text{or} \quad \frac{dB^2}{dr_0^2} > 0 \,.$$

(15.10)

Evidently the first condition is fulfilled from the outset, since we are here concerned with the positive damping. The second condition is the same as we have previously obtained in Section 6 (c).

16. Analysis of harmonic oscillations by means of integral curves [1, 9, 10, 38, 46, 47, 51]

As mentioned already, our object is to study the solution of equation (15.1) in the transient state, which, with the lapse of time, yields ultimately the periodic solution. For this purpose it is useful to investigate, following Poincaré

[25, 26, 48] and Bendixson [3], the integral curves of the following equation derived from (15.3), i. e.,

$$\frac{dy}{dx} = \frac{Y(x, y)}{X(x, y)}.$$
(16.1)

Since the time τ does not occur explicitly in this equation, we can draw the integral curves in the x, y-plane with the aid of the isocline method or otherwise.* As mentioned in the preceding section, periodic solutions are related with $x(\tau) =$ constant, $y(\tau) =$ constant of equations (15.3), and therefore with the singular points of equation (16.1), i. e., the points at which $X(x, y)$ and $Y(x, y)$ both vanish.

Now suppose that we fix a point $x(0)$, $y(0)$ in the x, y-plane as the initial condition. Then the point $x(\tau)$, $y(\tau)$ moves, with the lapse of time τ, on the integral curve which passes through the initial point $x(0)$, $y(0)$ and gets ultimately to a stable singular point.† Hence, the transient solutions are correlated with the integral curves of equation (16.1), and the steady (periodic) solutions with the singular points in the x, y-plane. The time variation of $v(\tau)$ in the transient state may be obtained by the line integral

$$\tau = \int \frac{ds}{\sqrt{X^2(x, y) + Y^2(x, y)}}, \qquad ds = \sqrt{(dx)^2 + (dy)^2},$$
(16.2)

where $X(x, y)$ and $Y(x, y)$ are given by equations (15.3), and ds is the line element on the integral curve.

We turn, for the time being, to a discussion of the character of the integral curves in the neighborhood of the singular points of equation (16.1). For the singular point, the roots of the characteristic equation (15.8) are given, by the use of (15.3), as

$$\lambda_{1, 2} = \frac{a_1 + b_2 \pm \sqrt{(a_1 - b_2)^2 + 4a_2 b_1}}{2},$$

---

* Another form of graphical solution has been given by Liénard [20].

† It is to be noticed that under certain conditions the point $x(\tau)$, $y(\tau)$ does not get to a singular point, but moves permanently on a closed trajectory in the x, y-plane. Occurrences of this kind were first studied by Poincaré [48, p. 53], who gave the name "limit cycle" to such a closed solution curve. However, as we shall see in Section 19, the integral curves of (16.1) have no limit cycle provided that the original differential equation is given by (15.1).

where

$$a_1 = \left(\frac{\partial X}{\partial x}\right)_{\substack{x=x_0, \\ y=y_0}} = \frac{1}{2}\left[-k-\frac{3}{2}x_0 y_0\right],$$

$$a_2 = \left(\frac{\partial X}{\partial y}\right)_{\substack{x=x_0, \\ y=y_0}} = \frac{1}{2}\left[1-\frac{3}{4}(x_0^2+3y_0^2)\right],$$

$$b_1 = \left(\frac{\partial Y}{\partial x}\right)_{\substack{x=x_0, \\ y=y_0}} = \frac{1}{2}\left[-1+\frac{3}{4}(3x_0^2+y_0^2)\right],$$

$$b_2 = \left(\frac{\partial Y}{\partial y}\right)_{\substack{x=x_0, \\ y=y_0}} = \frac{1}{2}\left[-k+\frac{3}{2}x_0 y_0\right].$$

(16.3)

Poincaré [48, p. 14] has classified the types of singular points according to the character of the integral curves near the singular points, *viz.*, according to the nature of the characteristic roots λ, as follows:

(1) The singularity is a nodal point, if the characteristic roots are both real and of the same sign, so that

$$(a_1-b_2)^2+4a_2 b_1 \geqq 0,$$

and

$$a_1 b_2 - a_2 b_1 > 0.$$

(16.4)

(2) The singularity is a saddle point, if the two roots are real but of opposite signs, so that

$$(a_1-b_2)^2+4a_2 b_1 > 0,$$

and

$$a_1 b_2 - a_2 b_1 < 0.$$

(16.5)

(3) The singularity is a spiral point, if the two roots are conjugate complex, so that

$$(a_1-b_2)^2+4a_2 b_1 < 0.$$

(16.6)

If, in particular, both the roots are purely imaginary so that $a_1+b_2 = 0$, the singularity is either a center or a spiral.*

---

* The term "focal point" is also used for a spiral point, and the term "vortex point" for a center. Poincaré [48, p. 95] has shown a rigorous criterion for distinguishing between a center and a spiral in the case when $(a_1-b_2)^2+4a_2 b_1 < 0$ and $a_1+b_2 = 0$.

We also infer a singularity to be stable or unstable according as a point on any integral curve moves into the said singularity or not with increasing τ, i.e., according as the real part of λ is negative or positive.

We shall illustrate the types of singularities in what follows. Figure 16.1a gives an example of a nodal point. In this example, the singular point is stable, since the point $x(\tau)$, $y(\tau)$ moves on the integral curves in the direction of the arrows as τ increases, and ultimately gets to the nodal point. The saddle point in Fig. 16.1b is a singularity which is terminated by four trajectories forming two distinct integral curves. Two of these trajectories approach the saddle point with increasing τ, while two others move away from it with increasing τ, so that the saddle point is intrinsically unstable. We also see that, between these trajectories, there exist four regions containing continua of hyperbolically-shaped integral curves which do not approach the singularity.

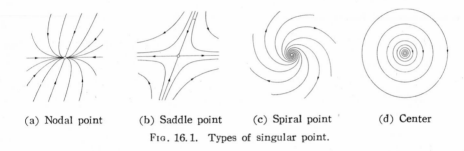

(a) Nodal point   (b) Saddle point   (c) Spiral point   (d) Center

FIG. 16.1. Types of singular point.

Figure 16.1c gives an example of an unstable spiral point from which the trajectories start without any definite direction. Finally, Fig. 16.1d shows a center which is surrounded by a continuum of closed curves such that none approaches it.

The integral curves of equation (16.1), particularly those in the neighborhood of the singular points, were elaborately studied by Poincaré [25, 26, 48] and Bendixson [3]. However, it is not the purpose of this book to describe these investigations in detail; we shall rather lay our stress on their application to the geometrical analysis of non-linear oscillations, and refer to the original papers as occasion demands.

We now turn to our present investigation. The relationship between B and r_0^2 are first calculated from equations (15.5) and plotted in Fig. 16.2 for several values of k. Following the foregoing classification, we shall distinguish these periodic states of equilibrium † according to the types of singularities.

---

† These periodic states of equilibrium are not necessarily sustained, but are able to last as long as they are correlated with stable singularities.

The boundary line between nodes and saddles is determined by equations (16.4) and (16.5) as

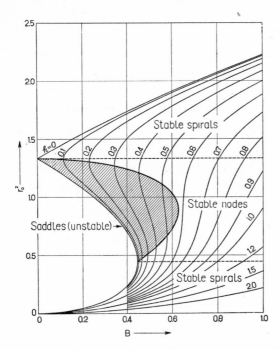

$$a_1 b_2 - a_2 b_1 = 0, \quad (16.7)$$

which, upon substituting equations (16.3), leads to

$$\frac{27}{16} r_0^4 - 3r_0^2 + k^2 + 1 = 0. \quad (16.8)$$

This equation is identical with $dB^2/dr_0^2 = 0$ [see equations (15.10)], and the region of the saddle points is marked by hatched lines where dB^2/dr_0^2 is negative. Since one of the roots λ is always positive, the periodic states in this region are unstable. This agrees with the result obtained in the preceding section.

Fig. 16.2. Amplitude characteristic of harmonic oscillation and correlated singularities.

Similarly, the boundary lines between nodes and spirals are determined by equations (16.4) and (16.6) as

$$(a_1 - b_2)^2 + 4a_2 b_1 = 0, \quad (16.9)$$

which, upon substituting equations (16.3), leads to

$$\frac{27}{16} r_0^4 - 3r_0^2 + 1 = 0, \quad \text{i. e.,} \quad r_0^2 = \frac{4}{3}, \ \frac{4}{9}. \quad (16.10)$$

These boundaries are shown by dotted lines in Fig. 16.2. Since, by equations (16.3), $a_1 + b_2 = -k$, it is readily seen that the periodic states of equilibrium in the regions of nodes and spirals are evidently stable.

17. Geometrical discussion of integral curves in special cases [10]

In the preceding section we have briefly referred to the transient solutions which are correlated with the integral curves of equation (16.1). It is, however, useful and illuminating to consider the integral curves for some exemplary cases. The special cases we have in mind are those specified by the following values of k and B in equation (15.1), namely,

$$\text{Case 1.} \quad k = 0.2, \quad B = 0.3,$$

and

$$\text{Case 2.} \quad k = 0.7, \quad B = 0.75.$$

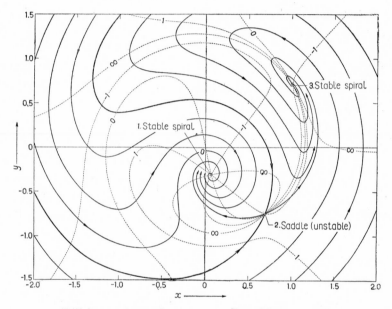

Full lines: integral curves   Dotted lines: isoclines

Fɪɢ. 17.1.   Integral curves for the harmonic oscillation with three singularities.

As observed in Fig. 16.2, there are three different states of equilibrium in the first case, whereas there is only one periodic state in the second case. The integral curves for these two cases are shown in Figs. 17.1 and 17.2, respectively. The singularities are determined by equations (15.4) and summed up in Table 17.1.

Tᴀʙʟᴇ 17.1.   Singular points in Figs. 17.1 and 17.2.

Singular point	x_0	y_0	λ_1, λ_2	μ_1, μ_2	Classification
Fig. 17.1, (1)	0.067	−0.310	−0.100 ± 0.423i	—	stable spiral
Fig. 17.1, (2)	0.699	−0.748	0.170, −0.370	0.392, 2.113	saddle (unstable)
Fig. 17.1, (3)	1.012	0.702	−0.100 ± 0.289i	—	stable spiral
Fig. 17.2	0.983	−0.295	−0.082, −0.618	1.275, −12.21	stable node

In this table μ_1, μ_2 represent the tangential slopes of the integral curves at the singular points. [For the derivation, see Appendix V(a).]

The integral curves in Figs. 17.1 and 17.2 are drawn with the aid of the isoclines represented by dotted-line curves, the numbers on which show the values of dy/dx for the respective isoclines. By equations (15.3), a point $x(\tau)$, $y(\tau)$ moves, with the lapse of time τ, on the integral curve in the direction of the arrows, and gets ultimately to the stable singular point.

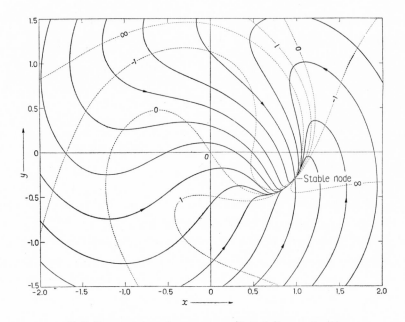

Full lines: integral curves   Dotted lines: isoclines

Fɪɢ. 17.2. Integral curves for the harmonic oscillation with one singularity.

In Fig. 17.1 we have three singularities; two of which, i.e., (1) and (3), are stable, and the corresponding periodic states are sustained. The remaining singularity (2) is a saddle point which is intrinsically unstable, and the corresponding periodic state cannot be sustained, because any slight deviation from the point (2) will lead the oscillation to the stable state represented by either the point (1) or (3). It is also clear that one of the integral curves (i.e., the thick-line curve in Fig. 17.1) which contains the saddle point (2) separates the whole plane into two regions, in one of which all integral curves tend to the singularity (1), while in the other to the singularity (3).

Figure 17.3 shows these regions in the r, θ-plane where r is the amplitude and θ is the phase angle of v at the instant the external force is impressed, i.e.,

$$r = \sqrt{x^2(0) + y^2(0)},$$

$$\theta = \arctan \frac{-y(0)}{x(0)}.$$

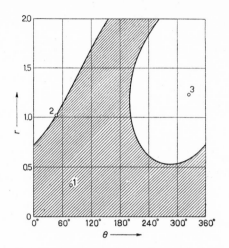

From this figure, the relationship between the initial conditions and the resulting oscillations is apparent; namely, an oscillation started with any initial conditions r and θ in the shaded region gets ultimately to the singularity (1), whereas an oscillation started from the unshaded region gets to the singularity (3). It is also seen that the singular point (2) is situated on the boundary curve between these two regions.

Fig. 17.3. Regions of initial conditions leading to resonant oscillation (unshaded) and non-resonant oscillation (shaded).

In Fig. 17.2 we have only one stable node, in other words, we have a single periodic solution for any initial conditions prescribed.

It is obvious by equations (16.3) that the amplitude and the phase angle of an oscillation in the neighborhood of the periodic state approach, with the lapse of time, the final state with damped sinusoids in the case when the corresponding singularity is a stable spiral, and approach the final state with damped exponentials in the case when the singularity is a stable node. We can also see from Figs. 17.1 and 17.2 that, when the initial value of r is comparatively large, the transient oscillation has a higher frequency than that of the impressed force, because the point $x(\tau)$, $y(\tau)$ correlated with that transient oscillation moves on an integral curve in the counter-clockwise direction around the origin O.

18.1. Further discussion for systems without damping

Although dissipation exists in all natural systems, the study of conservative systems will be of some value to us, first for the interesting character of their integral curves and second, as an introduction to the following non-conservative systems.

Putting $k = 0$ in equations (15.3), we have

$$\frac{dx}{d\tau} = \frac{1}{2}\left[B + y - \frac{3}{4}r^2 y\right] \equiv X(x,\,y)\,,$$

$$\frac{dy}{d\tau} = \frac{1}{2}\left[-x + \frac{3}{4}r^2 x\right] \equiv Y(x,\,y)\,,\qquad\qquad (18.1)$$

from which we obtain

$$Y(x,\,y)\,dx - X(x,\,y)\,dy = 0\,. \qquad\qquad (18.2)$$

Since by (18.1) $\dfrac{\partial X}{\partial x} + \dfrac{\partial Y}{\partial y} = 0$, equation (18.2) becomes an exact differential equation, and hence the complete integral is

$$\frac{3}{16}r^4 - \frac{1}{2}r^2 - By = C\,, \qquad\qquad (18.3)$$

C being a constant of integration. The integral curves of (18.1) are readily obtained by plotting (18.3), and an example will be given shortly.

Now, in order to investigate the integral curves in the neighborhood of a singular point in detail, we transfer the origin to the singular point x_0, y_0 by a change of the variables, i. e.,

$$x = x_0 + \xi\,, \qquad y = y_0 + \eta\,.$$

Then the fundamental equations (15.3) become

$$\frac{d\xi}{d\tau} = a_1\xi + a_2\eta - \frac{3}{8}\left(y_0\xi^2 + 2x_0\xi\eta + 3y_0\eta^2 + \xi^2\eta + \eta^3\right),$$

$$\frac{d\eta}{d\tau} = b_1\xi + b_2\eta + \frac{3}{8}\left(3x_0\xi^2 + 2y_0\xi\eta + x_0\eta^2 + \xi^3 + \xi\eta^2\right),$$

where

$$a_1 = \left(\frac{\partial X}{\partial x}\right)_{\substack{x=x_0,\\y=y_0}} = \frac{1}{2}\left[-k - \frac{3}{2}x_0 y_0\right],$$

$$a_2 = \left(\frac{\partial X}{\partial y}\right)_{\substack{x=x_0,\\y=y_0}} = \frac{1}{2}\left[1 - \frac{3}{4}(x_0^2 + 3y_0^2)\right], \qquad (18.4)$$

$$b_1 = \left(\frac{\partial Y}{\partial x}\right)_{\substack{x=x_0,\\y=y_0}} = \frac{1}{2}\left[-1 + \frac{3}{4}(3x_0^2 + y_0^2)\right],$$

$$b_2 = \left(\frac{\partial Y}{\partial y}\right)_{\substack{x=x_0,\\y=y_0}} = \frac{1}{2}\left[-k + \frac{3}{2}x_0 y_0\right].$$

These equations are generally applied to systems with and without damping, and reduced to equations (15.7) if we neglect the terms containing higher powers than the first in ξ, η.

Now, in our present case, putting $k = 0$ in (18.4), and remembering that $x_0 = 0$ from (15.6), we have

$$\frac{d\xi}{d\tau} = a_2\eta - \frac{3}{8}(y_0\xi^2 + 3y_0\eta^2 + \xi^2\eta + \eta^3),$$

$$\frac{d\eta}{d\tau} = b_1\xi + \frac{3}{8}(2y_0\xi\eta + \xi^3 + \xi\eta^2),$$

where

$$a_2 = \frac{1}{2}\left(1 - \frac{9}{4}y_0^2\right),$$

$$b_1 = \frac{1}{2}\left(-1 + \frac{3}{4}y_0^2\right).$$

$$(18.5)$$

These are readily integrated as in the case of equations (18.1), and we obtain

$$b_1\xi^2 - a_2\eta^2 + \frac{3}{4}\left[\frac{1}{4}(\xi^2 + \eta^2)^2 + y_0\eta(\xi^2 + \eta^2)\right] = C, \qquad (18.6)$$

C being a constant of integration.

In order to classify the types of singularities, we calculate λ_1, λ_2 from equations (16.3); they are

$$\lambda_1, \ \lambda_2 = \pm\sqrt{a_2 b_1}, \qquad a_1 + b_2 = 0. \quad (18.7)$$

The B, r_0^2–curve for $k = 0$ is reproduced in Fig. 18.1 (see Fig. 16.2). We divide this curve into three sections I, II, and III (as indicated in the figure) whose boundaries are given by the points A and B at which $r_0^2 = 4/3$ and $4/9$ respectively. We then have the following singularities for the respective sections, i.e.,

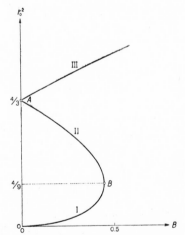

Fig. 18.1. Amplitude characteristic in non-dissipative system.

Section I: center* $(a_2 b_1 < 0)$,

Section II: saddle point $(a_2 b_1 > 0)$,

Section III: center* $(a_2 b_1 < 0)$.

---

* As has been pointed out by Poincaré [48, p. 95], the condition $a_1 + b_2 = 0$ is not sufficient to distinguish a center from a spiral point in the case when $a_2 b_1 < 0$; however, in our case, the singularity is certainly a center as can be seen by plotting (18.3) or (18.6).

Example:

We consider the case that $B = 0.2$. There are three kinds of equilibrium state (see Fig. 18.1), and the correlated singularities are summed up in Table 18.1.

TABLE 18.1.   Singular points for $B = 0.2$ (see Fig. 18.2).

Singular point	y_0	λ_1, λ_2	μ_1, μ_2	Classification
(1)	-0.207	$\pm 0.468i$	—	center (neutral)
(2)	-1.037	± 0.262	∓ 0.369	saddle (unstable)
(3)	1.244	$\pm 0.316i$	—	center (neutral)

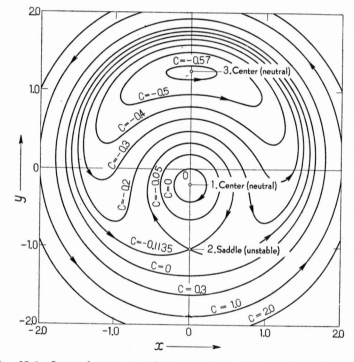

FIG. 18.2.   Integral curves for the harmonic oscillation without damping.

The integral curves of equations (18.1) are depicted in Fig. 18.2 by plotting (18.3) for various values of C. Now we see that, in a conservative system, each integral curve forms a closed trajectory and does not get to a stable singularity. Hence, with the lapse of time, the point $x(\tau)$, $y(\tau)$ which started from a given initial condition $x(0)$, $y(0)$, moves on the closed trajectory in the direction of the arrows, and comes back again to the initial point $x(0)$, $y(0)$, and after that, with further increase in the time, the point $x(\tau)$, $y(\tau)$ retraces the same trajectory repeatedly. This means that the amplitude and the phase angle of the correlated oscillation are no more constant but vary periodically with time in the steady state. Thus the phase angle of the oscillation may lead or lag the external force, but when the closed trajectory does not encircle the origin of the coordinates, the total leading and lagging angles cancel each other in every cycle in which the point $x(\tau)$, $y(\tau)$ makes one round on the closed trajectory, and so the oscillation is perfectly synchronized with the external force. While, on the other hand, when the closed trajectory contains the origin in its interior, a phase difference of 2π radians would result in every cycle mentioned above, and the oscillation is no longer synchronized with the external force.

We shall finally investigate those cases in which the systems are specified by the points A and B in Fig. 18.1.

(a) Integral curves in the case when the equilibrium state is represented by the point A

Putting $B = 0$ in equations (18.1), we have

$$\frac{dy}{dx} = -\frac{x}{y},$$

or integrating this,

$$x^2 + y^2 = \text{constant}.$$

Hence the integral curves are represented by a family of concentric circles whose center is the origin of the coordinates, and so the singularity (i. e., the origin in this case) is of the center type. The period T required for the point $x(\tau)$, $y(\tau)$ to make one round on these closed trajectories is given by

$$T = \oint \frac{ds}{\sqrt{X^2(x,\,y) + Y^2(x,\,y)}} = \oint \frac{ds}{\frac{1}{2}\left(1 - \frac{3}{4}r^2\right)r} = \frac{4\pi}{1 - \frac{3}{4}r^2}. \qquad (18.8)$$

Now, if we prescribe, as an initial condition, a point $x(0)$, $y(0)$ on the circle, the radius of which is given by $r = \sqrt{4/3}$, the period T would tend to infinity. As we see from equations (18.1), the point $x(\tau)$, $y(\tau)$ stays in this case at the initial position regardless of the lapse of time. This means that the frequency of the oscillation is the same as that of the external force. Further, from equations (18.1), we also see that the point $x(\tau)$, $y(\tau)$ moves in the counter-clockwise direction on the circle when $r^2 > 4/3$, and in the clockwise direction when $r^2 < 4/3$. In the former case, the oscillation has a higher

frequency than that of the external force, and in the latter case, the circumstances are reversed. Thus, in the end, we may conclude that the frequency
of the oscillation changes with varying r, and it coincides with the frequency
of the external force in the case of $r^2 = 4/3$ only.

(b) Integral curves in the case when the equilibrium state is represented by
the point B

In this case $k = 0$ and $B = 4/9$, and so, from equations (15.5) and (15.6),
we have

$$r_0^2 = \frac{4}{9}, \quad x_0 = 0, \quad \text{and} \quad y_0 = -\frac{2}{3}. \tag{18.9}$$

As illustrated in Fig. 16.2, the regions of nodes, spirals, and saddles come to-
gether at the point B. We shall investigate the character of this singular
point in what follows.*

From equations (16.3) and (18.5),

$$a_1 = a_2 = b_2 = 0, \quad b_1 = -\frac{1}{3},$$

and so we find that $\lambda_1 = \lambda_2 = 0$. From (18.5) the integral curves in the ξ, η-plane
is determined by

$$\left.\begin{array}{l} \dfrac{d\xi}{d\tau} = \dfrac{1}{4}\,(\xi^2 + 3\eta^2) - \dfrac{3}{8}\,(\xi^2\eta + \eta^3), \\[3mm] \dfrac{d\eta}{d\tau} = -\dfrac{1}{3}\,\xi - \dfrac{1}{2}\,\xi\eta + \dfrac{3}{8}\,(\xi^3 + \xi\eta^2), \end{array}\right\} \tag{18.10}$$

or, substituting $dz = b_1 d\tau = -\dfrac{1}{3}\,d\tau$ into (18.10), we have

$$\left.\begin{array}{l} \dfrac{d\xi}{dz} = -\dfrac{3}{4}\,(\xi^2 + 3\eta^2) + \dfrac{9}{8}\,(\xi^2\eta + \eta^3), \\[3mm] \dfrac{d\eta}{dz} = \xi + \dfrac{3}{2}\,\xi\eta - \dfrac{9}{8}\,(\xi^3 + \xi\eta^2). \end{array}\right\} \tag{18.11}$$

The integral curves in the ξ, η-plane tend to the origin with the tangent $\xi = 0$,
and so, by making use of the transformation $\xi = x_1\eta$, equations (18.11) lead to

$$\left.\begin{array}{l} \dfrac{dx_1}{dz} = -x_1^2 + \eta\left[-\dfrac{9}{4} + \dfrac{9}{8}\,\eta - \dfrac{9}{4}\,x_1^2 + \dfrac{9}{4}\,x_1^2\eta + \dfrac{9}{8}\,x_1^4\eta\right], \\[3mm] \dfrac{d\eta}{dz} = \eta\left[x_1 + \eta\left(\dfrac{3}{2}\,x_1 - \dfrac{9}{8}\,x_1\eta - \dfrac{9}{8}\,x_1^3\eta\right)\right]. \end{array}\right\} \tag{18.12}$$

---

* The following analysis refers to Appendix V and the contribution due to Bendixson
[3, pp. 58, 62, 74].

Now the integral curves in the x_1, η-plane tend to the origin with the tangent $\eta = 0$, and, by the further transformation $\eta = x_1 y_1$, equations (18.12) lead to

$$\left. \begin{aligned} \frac{dx_1}{dz} &= -x_1^2 - \frac{9}{4} x_1 y_1 + \left[-\frac{9}{4} x_1^3 y_1 + \frac{9}{8} x_1^2 y_1^2 + \frac{9}{4} x_1^4 y_1^2 + \frac{9}{8} x_1^6 y_1^2 \right], \\ \frac{dy_1}{dz} &= 2 x_1 y_1 + \frac{9}{4} y_1^2 + \left[\frac{15}{4} x_1^2 y_1^2 - \frac{9}{8} x_1 y_1^3 - \frac{27}{8} x_1^3 y_1^3 - \frac{9}{4} x_1^5 y_1^3 \right]. \end{aligned} \right\} \quad (18.13)$$

The tangents of the integral curves at the origin of the x_1, y_1-plane are determined by

$$x_1 y_1 \left(x_1 + \frac{3}{2} y_1 \right) = 0, \qquad \text{[see Appendix V (c)]}. \qquad (18.14)$$

However, in this equation, the tangents $x_1 = 0$ and $y_1 = 0$ are reduced to the origin $\xi = \eta = 0$ in the ξ, η-plane, and therefore we shall particularly investigate the integral curves which have the tangent $x_1 + (3/2) y_1 = 0$ at the origin. To effect this, we further introduce the transformation

$$y_1 = \left(y_2 - \frac{2}{3} \right) x_1$$

into (18.13), and obtain

$$x_1 \frac{dy_2}{dx_1} = \frac{-3 y_2 + \frac{9}{2} y_2^2 + x_1^2 \varphi (x_1, y_2)}{\frac{1}{2} - \frac{9}{4} y_2 + x_1 \psi (x_1, y_2)}, \qquad (18.15)$$

where $\varphi (x_1, y_2)$ and $\psi (x_1, y_2)$ are the polynomials in x_1, y_2. As mentioned in Appendix V (c), equation (18.15) has a form

$$x^m \frac{dy}{dx} = ay + bx + B (x, y),$$

where $B(x, y)$ contains terms of higher degree than the first in x, y, and for the case of equation (18.15) we have

$$m = 1 \quad \text{(an odd number)}, \quad \text{and} \quad a = -6 < 0,$$

so that the singularity $(x_1 = 0, y_2 = 0)$ is a saddle point,[†] and the integral curves tend to it with the tangents $x_1 = 0$ and $y_2 = 0$.

---

† There is another singularity $(x_1 = 0, y_2 = 2/3)$ for equation (18.15), but the investigation of this singularity is not necessary when we consider the integral curves in the ξ, η-plane.

Now, from the foregoing transformations, we have

$$\xi = x_1 \eta = x_1^2 y_1 = x_1^3 \left(y_2 - \frac{2}{3} \right),$$

$$\eta = x_1 y_1 = x_1^2 \left(y_2 - \frac{2}{3} \right).$$

As mentioned before, the tangent $x_1 = 0$ is reduced to the origin $\xi = \eta = 0$ in the ξ, η-plane, but the tangent $y_2 = 0$ is transformed to

$$\xi = -\frac{2}{3} x_1^3, \qquad \eta = -\frac{2}{3} x_1^2, \tag{18.16}$$

and these may be considered to represent the integral curves in the neighborhood of the origin in the ξ, η-plane. The tangent $y_2 = 0$ in the respective

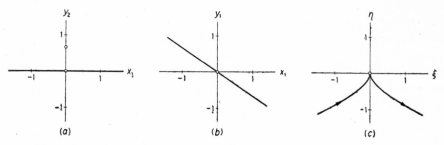

Fig. 18.3. Integral curves in their respective coordinates, the singularity being correlated with the point B in Fig. 18.1.

coordinates is illustrated in Fig. 18.3. There are two and only two branches of the integral curves which tend to the origin of the ξ, η-plane with the tangent $\xi = 0$, because, if there were more than two, there would be more than two branches of the integral curves tending to the origin of the x_1, y_2-plane with the tangent $y_2 = 0$, which contradicts the nature of the saddle point.

To summarize the conclusion, the singularity is a cusp, and, as we see from equations (18.10), a point $\xi(\tau), \eta(\tau)$ moves (with the lapse of time) on the integral curves in the direction of the arrows (see Fig. 18.3c), and so the equilibrium state correlated with this singular point is unstable. We may also notice that, with increasing B, the center (1) and the saddle point (2) of Fig. 18.2 approach each other, and finally the coalescence gives rise to a cusp.

18.2. Further discussion for systems with damping

We have previously considered the integral curves and the singular points correlated with the harmonic oscillations in non-conservative systems. As explained in Section 16, the types of singularities and their stability are distinct once the roots λ_1, λ_2 (different from zero) of the characteristic equation (15.8) are obtained. However, there still remains the particular case when either or both roots are zero. In this case, the corresponding singular points are said to be *of the second kind*. An example of such a singularity was already given as a cusp in Section 18.1 (b). As compared with these singularities, those for which both roots are not zero are said to be *simple* or *of the first kind*. In this section we shall consider some special cases of the harmonic oscillations and investigate the nature of the corresponding singular points in detail.

(a) Singular point on the boundaries between the regions of nodes and spirals (see Fig. 16.2)

As mentioned in Section 16, these boundaries are given by

$$r_0^2 = \frac{4}{3}, \ \frac{4}{9}, \qquad \text{[see equation (16.10)]}.$$

The characteristic roots λ_1, λ_2 are readily calculated from (16.3) and (16.9), which are

$$\lambda_1 = \lambda_2 = -\frac{1}{2}k. \tag{18.17}$$

Hence the singularity is a stable node, and the tangential direction of the integral curves at the singular point is uniquely determined [see Appendix V(a)].

(b) Singular point on the boundary between the regions of nodes and saddles (see Fig. 16.2)

This boundary is given by the condition $dB^2/dr_0^2 = 0$. Solving equation (16.8) for r_0^2, we get

$$r_0^2 = \frac{8 \pm 4\sqrt{1-3k^2}}{9}. \tag{18.18}$$

Calculating x_0^2 and y_0^2 by (15.6), and substituting them into (18.4), we have

$$\left.\begin{array}{l} a_1 = a_2 = 0, \\[2mm] b_1 = \dfrac{1}{3}\left[\dfrac{6k^2(2 \pm \sqrt{1-3k^2})}{1+3k^2 \mp \sqrt{1-3k^2}} - 1 \right], \\[3mm] b_2 = -k, \end{array}\right\} \tag{18.19}$$

so that the characteristic roots are

$$\lambda_1 = 0, \qquad \lambda_2 = -k. \tag{18.20}$$

Thus the singular point with which we are dealing is that of the second kind, and so we shall investigate the stability in what follows.

Equations (18.4) may be written in this case

$$\left.\begin{aligned}
\frac{d\xi}{d\tau} &= -\frac{3}{8}\,(y_0\xi^2+2x_0\xi\eta+3y_0\eta^2+\xi^2\eta+\eta^3)\,, \\[2mm]
\frac{d\eta}{d\tau} &= b_1\xi-k\eta+\frac{3}{8}\,(3x_0\xi^2+2y_0\xi\eta+x_0\eta^2+\xi^3+\xi\eta^2)\,,
\end{aligned}\right\} \tag{18.21}$$

or substituting $dz = -k\,d\tau$ into (18.21),

$$\left.\begin{aligned}
\frac{d\xi}{dz} &= X_1\,, \\[2mm]
\frac{d\eta}{dz} &= \eta-a\xi+Y_1\,, \\[4mm]
\text{where} \qquad\qquad & \\[2mm]
X_1 &= \frac{3}{8k}\,(y_0\xi^2+2x_0\xi\eta+3y_0\eta^2+\xi^2\eta+\eta^3)\,, \\[2mm]
Y_1 &= -\frac{3}{8k}\,(3x_0\xi^2+2y_0\xi\eta+x_0\eta^2+\xi^3+\xi\eta^2)\,, \\[2mm]
a &= b_1/k\,.
\end{aligned}\right\} \tag{18.22}$$

The tangents of the integral curves at the origin of the ξ, η-plane are determined by [see Appendix V(c)]

$$\xi\,(\eta-a\xi) = 0\,. \tag{18.23}$$

We shall first show that there are two and only two branches of the integral curves which tend to the origin with the tangent $\xi = 0$. By making use of the transformation $\xi = \varphi\eta$, equations (18.22) lead to

$$\left.\begin{aligned}
\frac{d\varphi}{dz} &= -\varphi+\frac{9}{8k}\,y_0\eta+X_2\,, \\[2mm]
\frac{d\eta}{dz} &= \eta+Y_2\,,
\end{aligned}\right\} \qquad . \tag{18.24}$$

where X_2 and Y_2 are the polynomials containing terms of higher degree than the first in φ, η. The characteristic equation becomes in this case

$$(\lambda+1)(\lambda-1) = 0\,,$$

so that the singularity is a saddle point. Hence there are four branches of the integral curves tending to the origin (i. e., the singular point), two of which are approximated by $\eta = 0$ in the neighborhood of the origin $\varphi = \eta = 0$, but these are reduced to the origin $\xi = \eta = 0$ of the ξ, η-plane. We have, therefore, two and only two branches of the integral curves tending to the origin $\xi = \eta = 0$ with the tangent $\xi = 0$, one of them being situated above and the other under the ξ-axis.

Now we may conclude that all the other integral curves which tend to the origin have the tangent $\eta - \alpha\xi = 0$. In order, therefore, to investigate them, we apply the transformation

$$\eta = (\alpha + \psi)\,\xi$$

to (18. 22), and get

$$\xi^2 \frac{d\psi}{d\xi} = \frac{\psi + \dfrac{Y_1}{\xi}}{\dfrac{X_1}{\xi^2}} - \xi\,(\alpha + \psi), \qquad (18.25)$$

or

$$\xi^2 \frac{d\psi}{d\xi} = a\psi + b\xi + B_1\,(\xi,\,\psi),$$

where

$$a = \frac{8k}{3}\,\frac{1}{2\alpha x_0 + (3\alpha^2 + 1)\,y_0}\,,$$

$$b = -\,\frac{3\,(1 + \alpha^2)\,(x_0 + \alpha y_0)}{2\alpha x_0 + (3\alpha^2 + 1)\,y_0}\,,$$

$$(18.26)$$

$B_1\,(\xi,\,\psi)$ being a series containing terms of higher degree than the first in ξ, ψ. This takes the form of equation (V. 14) in Appendix V with $m = 2$ (an even number).* Hence, dividing the ξ, ψ-plane into two regions along the ψ-axis, we see that all the integral curves tend to the origin on either side of the ψ-axis (which side it will be depending on the sign of a), and that, on the other side, one and only one branch of the integral curves tends to the origin, while all the others veer away from the origin. Therefore, in the end, we may conclude that the equilibrium state correlated with the singularity is unstable.

We shall further derive an approximate equation of the integral curves in the neighborhood of the singularity. By making use of the further transformation

$$p = \frac{1}{a}\,\xi\,, \qquad q = a\psi + b\xi\,,$$

---

* It is here assumed that $2\alpha x_0 + (3\alpha^2 + 1)y_0 \neq 0$.

equation (18. 26) becomes

$$p^2 \frac{dq}{dp} = q + B_1'(p, q),\qquad(18.27)$$

where $B_1'(p, q)$ contains terms of higher degree than the first in p, q, so that it may be neglected as compared with q, since we confine the discussion to the singular point and its vicinity alone. Integrating (18. 27) under this condition, we have

$$q = C \cdot e^{-\frac{1}{p}},\qquad(18.28)$$

C being a constant of integration, and, turning back to the original ξ, η-relation, we finally obtain

$$\eta = \left(a - \frac{b}{a}\,\xi + C' \cdot e^{-\frac{a}{\xi}}\right)\xi,\qquad C' = C/a.\qquad(18.29)$$

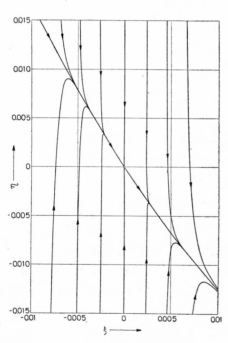

Fɪɢ. 18. 4. Coalescence of nodal point with saddle point resulting in a node-saddle distribution of the integral curves.

Example:

In order to illustrate the foregoing analysis, we consider a system with $k = 0.2$, say. Then, from (18. 18) we get

$$r_0^2 = 1.3058,\qquad 0.4720.$$

For the latter value of r_0^2 the following quantities are readily obtained; i. e.,

$$x_0 = \ 0.2032, \quad y_0 = -0.6563,$$
$$B = \ 0.4645, \quad \alpha = -1.460,$$
$$a = -0.0979, \quad b = \ 2.004.$$

Substituting these values into (18. 29), we can draw the integral curves for several values of C'. They are plotted in Fig. 18. 4. From equations (18. 21), we see that a point $\xi(\tau)$, $\eta(\tau)$ moves on the integral curves in the direction of the arrows. Thus a point $x(\tau)$, $y(\tau)$ tends to the origin in the region $\xi < 0$, but leaves the origin in the other region, *viz.*, $\xi > 0$. Hence, as already mentioned, the equilibrium state correlated with the singularity is unstable.

Now, in order to complete our discussion, we have to deal with the exceptional case in which

$$2ax_0 + (3a^2 + 1)\, y_0 = 0\,. \tag{18.30}$$

This takes place when equation (18.18) has two equal roots. In this case we have

$$1 - 3k^2 = 0\,, \quad \text{or} \quad k = \frac{1}{\sqrt{3}}\,,$$

and the following values which satisfy the condition (18.30) are readily obtained; namely,

$$r_0^2 = \frac{8}{9}\,, \qquad x_0 = \frac{\sqrt{2}}{\sqrt{3}}\,, \qquad y_0 = -\frac{\sqrt{2}}{3}\,, \qquad B = \frac{4\sqrt{2}}{9}\,,$$

$$a_1 = a_2 = 0\,, \qquad b_1 = \frac{1}{3}\,, \qquad b_2 = -\frac{1}{\sqrt{3}}\,,$$

$$\lambda_1 = -\frac{1}{\sqrt{3}}\,, \qquad \lambda_2 = 0\,.$$

Substituting these values into equation (18.25), we have

$$\xi^2 \frac{d\psi}{d\xi} = \frac{\psi - \sqrt{2}\,\xi - \dfrac{\sqrt{3}}{2}\,\xi^2 - \dfrac{3}{4}\,\xi^3\psi - \dfrac{3\sqrt{2}}{8}\,\xi\psi^2 - \dfrac{3\sqrt{3}}{8}\,\xi^2\psi^2}{\dfrac{1}{2}\,\xi + \dfrac{3\sqrt{3}}{4}\cdot\xi\psi - \dfrac{3\sqrt{6}}{8}\,\psi^2 + \dfrac{9}{8}\,\xi\psi^2 + \dfrac{3\sqrt{3}}{8}\,\xi\psi^3} - \frac{1}{\sqrt{3}}\,\xi - \xi\psi\,.$$

However, this does not take the form of equation (18.26), and so, applying the further transformation $\psi = (\sqrt{2} + \varphi)\,\xi$, we obtain

$$\xi^3 \frac{d\varphi}{d\xi} = \frac{\varphi - \dfrac{\sqrt{3}}{2}\,\xi - \dfrac{3}{4}\,\xi^2 (\sqrt{2} + \varphi) - \dfrac{3\sqrt{2}}{8}\,\xi^2(\sqrt{2} + \varphi)^2 - \dfrac{3\sqrt{3}}{8}\,\xi^3 (\sqrt{2} + \varphi)^2}{\dfrac{1}{2} + \dfrac{3\sqrt{3}}{4}\,\xi(\sqrt{2} + \varphi) - \dfrac{3\sqrt{6}}{8}\,\xi(\sqrt{2} + \varphi)^2 + \dfrac{9}{8}\,\xi^2(\sqrt{2} + \varphi)^2 + \dfrac{3\sqrt{3}}{8}\,\xi^3(\sqrt{2} + \varphi)^3}$$

$$- \frac{1}{\sqrt{3}}\,\xi - 2\xi^2 (\sqrt{2} + \varphi)\,,$$

or

$$\xi^3 \frac{d\varphi}{d\xi} = 2\varphi - \frac{4}{\sqrt{3}}\,\xi + B_2 (\xi, \varphi)\,, \tag{18.31}$$

where $B_2(\xi, \varphi)$ contains terms of higher degree than the first. This takes the form of equation (V. 14) in Appendix V with $m = 3$ (odd) and $a = 2 > 0$, and so the singularity is a nodal point. In order to find the integral curves in the neighborhood of the singularity, we further put

$$p = \frac{1}{\sqrt{2}}\xi, \qquad q = 2\varphi - \frac{4}{\sqrt{3}}\xi.$$

Equation (18.31) may then be written in the form

$$p^3 \frac{dq}{dp} = q + B_2'(p, q), \tag{18.32}$$

where $B_2'(p, q)$ contains terms of higher degree than the first. Hence, neglecting this, we integrate (18.32) and obtain

$$q = C \cdot e^{-\frac{1}{2p^2}},$$

C being a constant of integration, and in the ξ, η-plane

$$\eta = \left(\frac{1}{\sqrt{3}} + \sqrt{2}\,\xi - \frac{2}{\sqrt{3}}\xi^2 + \frac{C}{2}\xi\, e^{-\frac{1}{\xi^2}}\right)\xi. \tag{18.33}$$

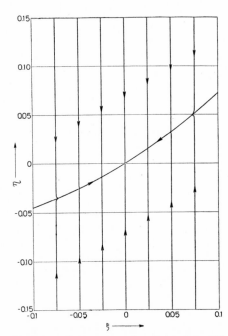

Fig. 18.5. Coalescence of nodal point with saddle point resulting in a nodal distribution of the integral curves.

The integral curves are computed for several values of C, and plotted in Fig. 18.5. From equations (18.21), we see that a point $x(\tau)$, $y(\tau)$ which started from any initial condition $x(0)$, $y(0)$ moves on the integral curve in the direction of the arrows, and tends ultimately to the origin. Hence, the singular point (i.e., the origin) and the correlated equilibrium state are stable.

In the end, we conclude that an equilibrium state correlated with the singular point on the boundary of the regions of nodes and saddles is usually unstable and changes over to another stable state; however, in the case when $k = 1/\sqrt{3}$ and $r_0^2 = 8/9$, the equilibrium state becomes stable. This is a plausible result from the physical point of view, since there is no other equilibrium state in this particular case (see Fig. 16. 2).

19. Integral curves with limit cycle—Quasi-periodic oscillation

Thus far we have dealt with the integral curves or the trajectories of a point $x(\tau)$, $y(\tau)$ which usually terminate in a singular point. We have also dealt with the closed trajectories only in the case of conservative systems where they always made up a whole continuum of concentric loops around a center (see Section 18.1). In certain non-conservative systems, however, we found closed trajectories or limit cycles towards which the neighboring trajectories spiral on both sides. In this section we shall investigate such a case and see what type of oscillation will be correlated with a limit cycle.

For a given non-linear system governed by

$$\frac{dx}{d\tau} = X(x, y), \qquad \frac{dy}{d\tau} = Y(x, y), \tag{19.1}$$

the problem of establishing the existence of a limit cycle is generally very difficult. However, it is often important to know that no limit cycle can exist, and the following Bendixson's criterion [3, p. 78] which establishes a condition for the non-existence of closed trajectories is quite useful in some cases.

Bendixson's criterion: if the expression $\partial X/\partial x + \partial Y/\partial y$ does not change its sign within a domain D of the x, y-plane, no closed trajectories can exist in that domain.

The proof is immediate. Suppose a closed curve such as γ existed in D. By the well known theorem of Gauss, if D' is the domain bounded by γ, then

$$\iint_{D'} \left(\frac{\partial X}{\partial x} + \frac{\partial Y}{\partial y}\right) dx\, dy = \oint_{\gamma} (X dy - Y dx) \neq 0. \tag{19.2}$$

However, along the path γ equation (19.1) holds, and so $X dy - Y dx = 0$. Hence the simple integral is zero. This contradiction proves the criterion.

Now turning back to equation (15.1), we find from (15.3) that

$$\frac{\partial X}{\partial x} + \frac{\partial Y}{\partial y} = -k. \tag{19.3}$$

Hence we see that the system (15.3) has no closed trajectories in the case of $k \neq 0$. When $k = 0$ (namely, in conservative systems), we have a continuum of closed trajectories around a center, but no limit cycles (see Section 18.1). We can also verify that in the case when the original equation is given by

$$\frac{d^2v}{d\tau^2} + k\frac{dv}{d\tau} + f(v) = B\cos\tau,\qquad(19.4)$$

where the non-linear restoring force $f(v)$ is expressed by a polynomial in v, the corresponding set of equations (19.1) has still no limit cycles.

Hence, in the following, we consider the case in which the damping coefficient k is a non-linear function in v. A typical example illustrating the application of the limit cycle, is found in van der Pol's investigation [27] related to a vacuum tube oscillator possessing a cubic characteristic. He has derived the differential equation

$$\frac{d^2v}{d\tau^2} - \varepsilon(1-v^2)\frac{dv}{d\tau} + v = 0,\qquad(19.5)$$

$\varepsilon\,(>0)$ being a constant, and treated the self-excited oscillation as correlated with the limit cycle in the $v, dv/d\tau$-plane.

We shall now take a differential equation involving, in addition to a non-linear damping, a non-linear restoring force and an external excitation. We thus consider a more general type of equation

$$\frac{d^2v}{d\tau^2} - \varepsilon(1-av^2)\frac{dv}{d\tau} + v^3 = B\cos\tau,\qquad(19.6)$$

where ε and a are both positive constants.

Proceeding in the same manner as in Section 15, we assume a solution in the form

$$v(\tau) = x(\tau)\sin\tau + y(\tau)\cos\tau,\qquad(19.7)$$

and substituting this into (19.6), we obtain

$$\left.\begin{aligned}
\frac{dx}{d\tau} &= \frac{1}{2}\,[B+kx-Ay] \equiv X(x,y),\\[2mm]
\frac{dy}{d\tau} &= \frac{1}{2}\,[Ax+ky] \equiv Y(x,y),
\end{aligned}\right\}\qquad(19.8)$$

where

$$\left.A = \frac{3}{4}\,r^2-1,\quad k = \varepsilon\left(1-\frac{a}{4}\,r^2\right),\quad r^2 = x^2+y^2,\right.$$

under the same restrictions as stated in Section 15. The equilibrium states in which the amplitudes $x(\tau)$, $y(\tau)$ are constant may be correlated with the singularities for which $X(x,y) = Y(x,y) = 0$ simultaneously. By making use of these relations, the amplitude r_0 of the periodic solution will be determined from (19.8), namely,

$$(A^2+k^2)\,r_0^2 = B^2\,. \tag{19.9}$$

From equations (19.8), we obtain

$$\begin{aligned}
\frac{\partial X}{\partial x} &= \frac{1}{2}\left[\varepsilon - \frac{a\varepsilon}{4}\,(3x^2+y^2) - \frac{3}{2}\,xy\right], \\[6pt]
\frac{\partial X}{\partial y} &= \frac{1}{2}\left[1 - \frac{3}{4}\,(x^2+3y^2) - \frac{a\varepsilon}{2}\,xy\right], \\[6pt]
\frac{\partial Y}{\partial x} &= \frac{1}{2}\left[-1 + \frac{3}{4}\,(3x^2+y^2) - \frac{a\varepsilon}{2}\,xy\right], \\[6pt]
\frac{\partial Y}{\partial y} &= \frac{1}{2}\left[\varepsilon - \frac{a\varepsilon}{4}\,(x^2+3y^2) + \frac{3}{2}\,xy\right].
\end{aligned}\right\} \tag{19.10}$$

The integral curves in the neighborhood of the singularities and consequently the stability of the equilibrium states will be distinct once the characteristic equation (15.8) is solved for λ. From equations (19.10), we have

$$\frac{\partial X}{\partial x} + \frac{\partial Y}{\partial y} = \varepsilon\left(1 - \frac{a}{2}\,r^2\right), \tag{19.11}$$

which may change in sign according to the values of r. It should be noticed that Bendixson's criterion is not sufficient to prove the existence of limit cycles; however, as will be illustrated presently, the system (19.8) may have a limit cycle provided that the values of ε, a, and B are properly chosen.

Example:

Let us consider the case in which

$$\varepsilon = 0.2, \quad \text{and} \quad a = 8\,.$$

Substituting these values into equations (19.8) and (19.9), the B, r_0^2–relation is calculated and plotted in Fig. 19.1. As illustrated in the figure, there are three singularities (1), (2), and (3) for $B = 0.35$. As in the case of Section 17, the details of the singularities are readily known and are shown in Table 19.1.

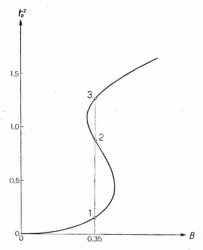

Fig. 19.1. Relationship between r_0^2 and B in (19.9).

TABLE 19.1. Singular points in Fig. 19.2.

Singular point	x_0	y_0	λ_1, λ_2	μ_1, μ_2	Classification
(1)	-0.061	-0.386	$0.039 \pm 0.380i$	—	unstable spiral
(2)	0.379	-0.857	$0.087, -0.589$	$2.802,\ \ 0.096$	saddle (unstable)
(3)	1.111	-0.180	$-0.111, -0.702$	$4.765, -2.538$	stable node

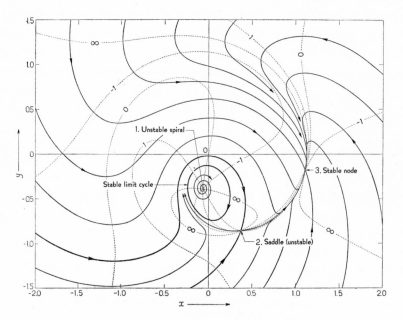

Full lines: integral curves   Dotted lines: isoclines

FIG. 19.2. Integral curves for the harmonic oscillation with limit cycle.

Contrary to the case as illustrated in Fig. 17.1 (see Section 17), the spiral point (1) becomes unstable, because, as we see in equation (19.6), the system has a negative damping for small values of r_0. By the use of equations (V.7), (V.8), and (V.9) in Appendix V, the integral curves in the neighborhood of the singular point (1) satisfy the relations (in polar coordinates r and θ)

$$r(\theta + 2\pi) = e^{\sigma \cdot 2\pi M} \cdot r(\theta) = 0.525 \ r(\theta),$$

and

$$\frac{d\theta}{d\tau} < 0.$$

Hence we see that a point $r(\tau)$, $\theta(\tau)$ moves on the integral curve in the clockwise direction around the singular point and gets away from it with the lapse of time.

In Fig. 19.2 we plot the integral curves of

$$\frac{dy}{dx} = \frac{Y(x, y)}{X(x, y)}$$

derived from equations (19.8) by making use of the isocline method. Thus we find there a limit cycle which encircles the unstable spiral point (1), and towards which the neighboring trajectories spiral on both sides. Hence, the limit cycle is stable in this case. It is also clear that one of the integral curves (i.e., the thick-line curve in Fig. 19.2) which contains the saddle point (2) separates the whole plane into regions, in one of which all integral curves tend to the limit cycle and in the other to the nodal point (3). In the latter

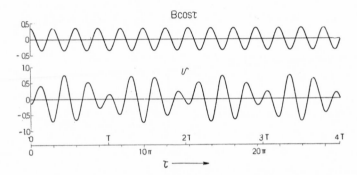

Fɪɢ. 19.3. Quasi-periodic oscillation represented by the limit cycle of Fig. 19.2.

case the amplitude and the phase angle of the oscillation become constant as the point $x(\tau)$, $y(\tau)$ tends to the singularity, while in the former case they keep on varying periodically with the time as the point correlated with the oscillation moves on the limit cycle repeatedly. From equations (19.8) the time variation of $v(\tau)$ along the limit cycle may be obtained by the line integral

$$\tau = \int \frac{ds}{\sqrt{X^2(x, y) + Y^2(x, y)}},$$

$$ds = \sqrt{(dx)^2 + (dy)^2} : \text{line element on the limit cycle.}$$

Thus we obtain Fig. 19.3, in which $v(\tau)$ is correlated with the limit cycle in Fig. 19.2. The period T required for the point $x(\tau)$, $y(\tau)$ to travel one complete cycle on the limit cycle (that is to say, the period of variation of the amplitude or the phase angle) is given by

$$T = \oint \frac{ds}{\sqrt{X^2(x,\ y) + Y^2(x,\ y)}} = 21.528 \cdots = 2\pi \times 3.426 \cdots .$$

Since it may be expected that the period T changes continuously with varying B (or other conditions such as ε or a), the ratio $T/(2\pi)$ is, in general, an irrational number. Hence the oscillation is not really periodic. However, after a sufficiently long period of time, the oscillation may represent a very close condition to that of the initial state, so that the oscillation may be said to be quasi-periodic. We also see in Fig. 19.2 that the limit cycle does not contain the origin of the coordinates in its interior, and so, as explained in Section 18.1, the oscillation is perfectly synchronized with the external force in this case.

20.   Experimental investigation [10, 32]

(a)   Relationship between the initial conditions and the resulting oscillations

As we have already mentioned in Section 1, it is a salient feature of non-linear oscillations that different types of steady state may be sustained by changing only the initial conditions with which the oscillations were started. In Fig. 1.1 cited there, for example, we see three types of oscillation; namely, two kinds of harmonic oscillation and a subharmonic oscillation of order 1/3, which are obtained in an electrical circuit containing a non-linear inductance.

We shall here perform experiments on a similar circuit (the details to be illustrated presently) and determine the regions of initial conditions which give rise to the respective types of periodic oscillation. However, we here confine our attention to the harmonic oscillations only, and the occurrence of the subharmonics will be treated later in Chapter VI.

Now we shall proceed to show some experimental results which are effective in verifying the foregoing analysis. As we have already evinced in Fig. 17.1, there are two kinds of stable oscillation correlated with the singularities (1) and (3). In Section 6 we have distinguished these as the resonant and the non-resonant states according as the amplitude of the oscillation is large or small. It is consequently clear that the singularity (3) in Fig. 17.1 is correlated with the resonant state and the singularity (1) with the non-resonant state.

In the foregoing analysis the initial conditions were prescribed with the sine and cosine components of $v(0)$, i.e., the coordinates $x(0)$, $y(0)$ of the initial point in the x, y-plane. This, however, is not practical for our present experiment, so that we prescribe the initial condition, instead, with the initial charging voltage across the condenser and the phase angle of the applied voltage at the instant it is impressed on the circuit. The schematic diagram illustrated in Fig. 20.1 shows an electrical circuit used for our experiment. The initial charging voltage V_{co} across the condenser C may readily be supplied from the battery E_1 by closing momentarily the switch SW_1. With regard to the other initial condition, an ordinary mechanical contactor would not suffice for closing the circuit at any desired phase angle of the applied voltage, so that, in order to effect the accurate timing, we use an electronic switch consisting of two thyratrons V_1, V_2 connected in inverse-parallel. These tubes are made conductive by impressing a potential on the grids at the desired phase angle of the applied voltage.*

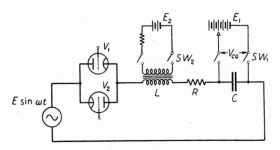

FIG. 20.1. Experimental circuit with means provided for prescribing the initial conditions.

It is also a noteworthy fact that the residual magnetism in the saturable core has a serious influence on the experiment. Therefore it should be demagnetized or at least held constant, and if this precaution is neglected, random result would be obtained in every experiment. Hence, as illustrated in Fig. 20.1, the inductance core is provided with a secondary winding through which a direct current flows from the battery E_2 upon closing the switch SW_2. Thus, prior to each experiment, the iron core is premagnetized in a certain direction by letting an

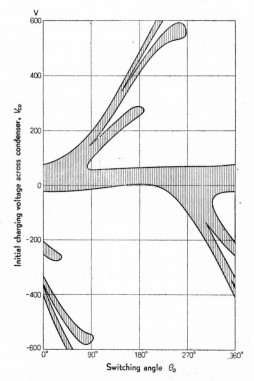

FIG. 20.2. Regions of initial conditions which give rise to resonant oscillation (unshaded) and non-resonant oscillation (shaded).

---

* For further details on the control circuit, the reader should refer to Appendix VI.

ample current flow through the secondary winding, and a constant residual magnetism is obtained after opening the switch SW_2.

Following this procedure we perform the experiment by starting the oscillations with various combinations of the initial conditions V_{co} and θ_0 (θ_0 being the switching angle of the applied voltage) and obtained Fig. 20.2. In the figure the shaded region corresponds to the initial conditions which give rise to the non-resonant state, and the remaining blank region corresponds to

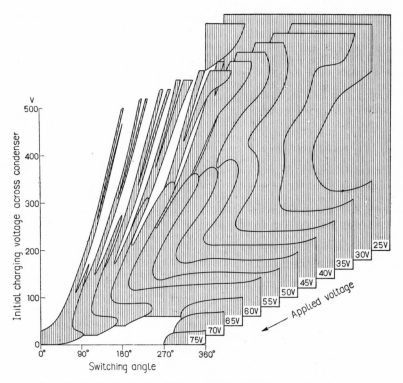

Fig. 20.3. Regions of initial conditions which give rise to resonant oscillation (unshaded) and non-resonant oscillation (shaded) obtained under different values of the applied voltage.

those of the resonant state. It will be noticed that the shaded region is shifted to some extent above the abscissa owing to the unidirectional premagnetization. Hence, if the core is completely demagnetized prior to each experiment, this figure should be symmetrical with respect to the abscissa when we shift the figure for $V_{co} < 0$ horizontally by 180 degrees in the direction of the θ_0-axis.

Similar experiments are further carried out for several values of the applied voltage, and the result is plotted in Fig. 20.3. As may be expected from the preceding analysis (see Fig. 16.2), the shaded regions (related to the non-resonant state) are contracted with the increase of the applied voltage. It is, however, to be noticed that even with an exceedingly high value of V_{co}, the non-resonant state may still result if we choose appropriately the initial switching angle θ_0. These experimental results are in accordance with the preceding analysis except for some slight discrepancies such as the branching of the shaded regions (see Fig. 17.3).

(b) Oscillations correlated with limit cycle

We shall, in the following, observe some oscillations whose amplitude and phase angle are not constant but vary periodically with time. Thus the oscillations with which we are going to deal are correlated with limit cycle.

The circuit used for our present purpose is the same as that illustrated in Fig. 7.4 except that the reactance of the secondary d–c circuit is held low by eliminating the reactor L. Hence, a considerable amount of the second harmonic current would be superimposed on the direct current, and further, for certain values of V_{ac} and I_{dc}, the current in the secondary circuit oscillates with a low frequency, and consequently the amplitude and phase angle of I_{ac} vary simultaneously. Such an anomalous oscillation may also be obtained in the alternative circuit as illustrated in Fig. 20.4.

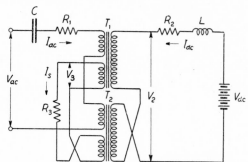

FIG. 20.4. Oscillatory circuit containing reactors with secondary d-c windings and tertiary circuit.

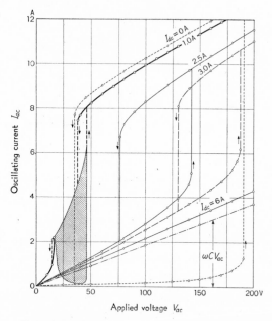

FIG. 20.5. Amplitude characteristic of harmonic oscillation, hatched part showing the range of beat oscillation.

In the figure the reactance of the secondary circuit is high owing to the presence of L, but the tertiary windings which are provided on the respective cores are connected in series (with opposite polarity) through a low resistance R_3 to annul the effect of the inductance L.

Proceeding as in Section 7.2, we first seek the relationship between V_{ac} and I_{ac} in Fig. 20.4 for several values of I_{dc} and the result is plotted in Fig. 20.5. In the case when $I_{dc} = 1.0$ amp., we see that, for a certain interval of V_{ac}, the

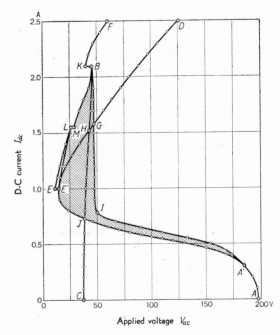

$AA'IGD$: boundary line on which resonant oscillation starts when increasing V_{ac}

$CJHBKF$: boundary line on which resonant oscillation stops when decreasing V_{ac}

$A'JE'HG$: boundary line on which beat oscillation starts when increasing V_{ac}

$A'IGB$: boundary line on which beat oscillation stops when increasing V_{ac}

JHB: boundary line on which beat oscillation starts when decreasing V_{ac}

$A'JE'LMB$: boundary line on which beat oscillation stops when decreasing V_{ac}

EL: transition line from subresonant to non-resonant oscillation when decreasing V_{ac}

FIG. 20.6. Regions of different types of oscillation.

amplitude of the oscillation is no more constant but varies periodically to the extent of the hatched area. This anomalous phenomenon presents a type of beat oscillation, whose wave form will be shown shortly. The subresonant state which was mentioned in Section 7.2 is hardly observed in the present case, and the beat oscillation is considered to replace it.

Further, the regions in which the oscillations of different types obtain are plotted in Fig. 20.6. The beat oscillation occurs in the hatched area and most remarkably in the range of $I_{dc} = 0.8 \sim 2.1$ amp. Further details are explained in the legend annexed to the figure.

The wave forms of the beat oscillation are illustrated in Fig. 20.7. Oscillogram (a) is taken in the circuit of Fig. 7.4, while (b) to (d) are taken with

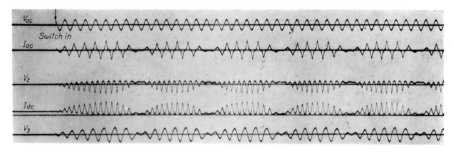

(a) Oscillation obtained in the circuit illustrated in Fig. 7.4

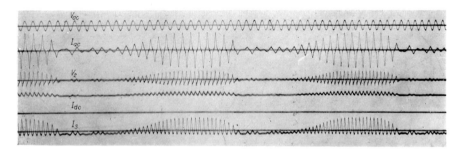

(b) Oscillation obtained in the circuit illustrated in Fig. 20.4 (R_3=1.5 Ω)

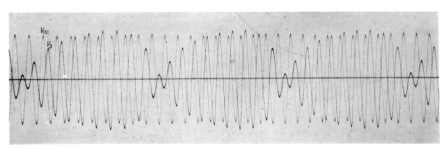

(c) Beat frequency 6.0 c.p.s. (R_3=4.7 Ω)

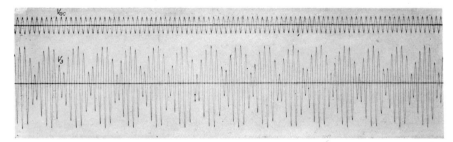

(d) Beat frequency 10.59 ··· c.p.s. (R_3=17.9 Ω)

Fɪɢ. 20.7. Beat oscillations.

increasing R_3 in Fig. 20.4. We see in these oscillograms that the amplitude of I_{ac} and others are slowly varying, presenting thus a type of beat oscillation, and also that the frequency of the variation, i.e., the beat frequency, is raised with the increase in R_3. In the preceding analysis we have set up the circuit equation with respect to the magnetic flux in the core, and it is the voltage V_3 (see Fig. 20.4) that is directly related to the flux since the time-derivative of the flux is proportional to V_3. Thus in Oscillogram (c) the wave form of

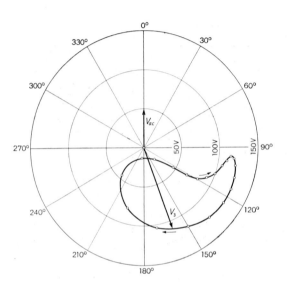

FIG. 20.8. Trajectory of the voltage vector V_3.

V_3 is closely observed with respect to that of V_{ac} and their vectorial representation is given in Fig. 20.8. Taking V_{ac} as the reference vector, the extremity of the vector V_3 moves on the closed trajectory (which is a limit cycle in this case) in the direction of the arrows. The period of one beat or the time interval required to make one complete round on the trajectory is, in this particular case, ten times the period of the applied voltage V_{ac}. Contrary to the case of subharmonic oscillations, however, there is no entrainment between these two periods.

In Oscillogram (d) the ratio of the periods is $5.76\cdots$, and the oscillation never repeats the same cycle, but gives rise to a quasi-periodic oscillation. However, the oscillation is perfectly synchronized with the applied voltage since the closed trajectory does not contain the origin in its interior.

CHAPTER VI

SUBHARMONIC OSCILLATIONS

21. Analysis of subharmonic oscillations by means of integral curves

In the preceding chapter we considered the transient state of harmonic oscillations and gave full details on the stability of equilibrium states correlated with singular points. We are now to deal with the subharmonic oscillations whose fundamental frequency is a fraction, $1/2$, $1/3$, $\cdots$, of that of the external force. As already mentioned in Capter IV, such oscillations may occur in non-linear systems, particularly in the case when the system is governed by the original equation (15.1).

As a typical example of analysis of the subharmonic oscillations by means of integral curves, we shall treat in this chapter only one special case, i.e., the subharmonic oscillation of order $1/3$ which is most frequently encountered in an oscillatory circuit containing saturable iron-cores.*

Consider the differential equation

$$\frac{d^2v}{d\tau^2} + k\frac{dv}{d\tau} + v^3 = B\cos 3\tau , \qquad (21.1)$$

in which we choose the argument of the external force to be 3τ instead of τ, in order to prepare for the study of the subharmonic oscillation of order $1/3$.

Proceeding in the same manner as in Section 15, the solution of equation (21.1) is assumed of the form

$$v(\tau) = x(\tau)\sin\tau + y(\tau)\cos\tau + w\cos 3\tau , \qquad (21.2)$$

where the amplitudes $x(\tau)$ and $y(\tau)$ are both functions of τ in the transient state, but are reduced to constants in the steady state. Following Mandelstam and Papalexi [21, p. 227], the amplitude w may be assumed to be

$$w = \frac{1}{1-3^2}B = -\frac{1}{8}B . \qquad (21.3)$$

Substituting (21.2) into (21.1) and equating the terms containing $\sin\tau$ and $\cos\tau$ separately to zero, we obtain

---

* Subharmonic oscillations of other orders are similarly treated provided that the appropriate non-linear characteristics are assumed (see Setion 11).

$$\frac{dx}{d\tau} = \frac{1}{2}\left[-kx + Ay + \frac{3}{4}w(x^2 - y^2) \right] \equiv X(x, y),$$

$$\frac{dy}{d\tau} = -\frac{1}{2}\left[Ax + ky + \frac{3}{4}w \cdot 2xy \right] \equiv Y(x, y),$$

$$\text{(21.4)}$$

where

$$A = 1 - \frac{3}{4}r^2 - \frac{3}{2}w^2, \qquad r^2 = x^2 + y^2.$$

It should, however, be remembered that the same restrictions as those mentioned in Section 15 must be assumed for the derivation of the above equations (21.4).

Now the oscillations in the steady state are correlated with the singular points determined by

$$X(x, y) = 0, \quad Y(x, y) = 0, \tag{21.5}$$

and the transient solution can be discussed by the integral curves of

$$\frac{dy}{dx} = \frac{Y(x, y)}{X(x, y)}, \tag{21.6}$$

where $X(x, y)$ and $Y(x, y)$ are given by equations (21.4).

The detailed investigation of the stability of equilibrium states which are correlated with the singular points of the second kind may also be carried out in the same manner as in Sections 18.1 and 18.2. However, we shall here refrain from entering into this problem and only show an illustrative example of the integral curves for the subharmonic oscillation of order 1/3.

Example:

We consider a case in which

$$k = 0.2 \quad \text{and} \quad B = 3.2.$$

Then, by equation (21.3), $w = -0.4$. Substituting these values into (21.4), the integral curves of equation (21.6) are plotted in Fig. 21.1 by making use of the isocline method. In the figure we see seven singular points, which are also determined directly from equations (21.5) and are shown in Table 21.1.

In Fig. 21.1 we see that the three singular points (1), (2), ane (3) are correlated with the subharmonic oscillation, and that they are all equidistant from the origin $x = 0$, $y = 0$, the angular distance between any two of these singular points being equal to 120 degrees, or equal to one complete cycle of the external force. This is a plausible result for the subharmonic oscillation of order 1/3.

As we also see from the integral curves in Fig. 21.1, an oscillation started from a point $x(0)$, $y(0)$ (which prescribes the initial condition) in the shaded regions gets ultimately to one of the singularities (1), (2), and (3) correlated with the subharmonic response, whereas any oscillation started from the unshaded region gets ultimately to the singularity (7). Since, at the singular point (7), $x = 0$, $y = 0$, no subharmonic oscillation takes place in this case. Thus

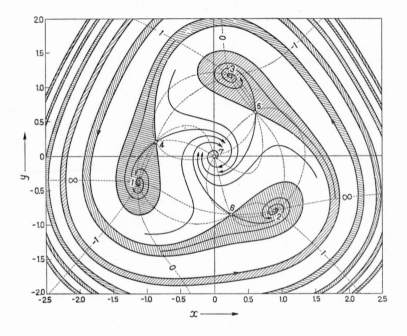

Full lines: integral curves   Dotted lines: isoclines

Fɪɢ. 21.1. Integral curves for the subharmonic oscillation of order 1/3.

Tᴀʙʟᴇ 21.1. Singular points of Fig. 21.1.*

Singular point	x_0	y_0	λ_1, λ_2	μ_1, μ_2	Classification
(1)	-1.123	-0.378	$-0.100 \pm 0.599i$	—	stable spiral
(2)	0.889	-0.784	$-0.100 \pm 0.599i$	—	stable spiral
(3)	0.234	1.162	$-0.100 \pm 0.599i$	—	stable spiral
(4)	-0.858	0.209	$0.365, -0.565$	$0.613, -7.274$	saddle (unstable)
(5)	0.610	0.639	$0.365, -0.565$	$-35.24, -0.407$	saddle (unstable)
(6)	0.248	-0.848	$0.365, -0.565$	$-0.543, 0.767$	saddle (unstable)
(7)	0	0	$-0.100 \pm 0.500i$	—	stable spiral

* See Section 17 for the notation.

the relationship between the initial conditions and the resulting oscillations is apparent.

Similar to the case of the harmonic oscillations, the time variation of $v(\tau)$ in the transient state is determined by the line integral (16.2) in Section 16. When the initial condition is given by a point far from the origin, the oscillation in the transient state has a higher frequency than in the steady state, because the point $x(\tau)$, $y(\tau)$ correlated with the transient oscillation moves on the integral curve in the counter-clockwise direction around the origin.

22. Experimental investigation

Referring back to the electrical circuit in Fig. 20.1, we shall compare the theoretical results of the foregoing analysis with experiments.

We first determine the region in which the subharmonic oscillation of order 1/3 is maintained in a stable state, by varying the applied voltage V and the capacitance C of the oscillatory circuit. The experimental result is shown in Fig. 22.1 where this region is indicated by hatched lines. We also determine the regions in which the resonant and the non-resonant harmonic oscillations are sustained. In Fig. 22.1 is drawn the curve ABC which shows the boundary of these regions. An oscillation which is first in the non-resonant state at a comparatively low voltage is transferred into the resonant state when the voltage is raised up to the boundary BC. On the contrary, a transition takes place from the resonant to the non-resonant state when the voltage is reduced down to the boundary AB. Hence, within the boundary curve ABC shaded by dotted lines, either the resonant or the non-resonant state may occur according to the initial conditions prescribed.

In what follows we shall consider the transient state of the subharmonic oscillation of order 1/3 and the regions of initial conditions which give rise to the above-mentioned types of oscillation.

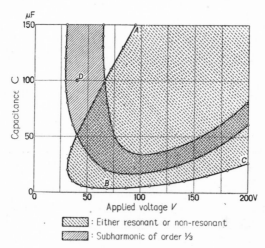

: Either resonant or non-resonant
: Subharmonic of order ⅓

Fig. 22.1. Regions in which the oscillations of different types are sustained.

(a)   Initial conditions leading either to the non-resonant or to the subharmonic oscillation

As evinced in Fig. 22.1, there are two periodic states of oscillation, *viz.*, those of the non-resonant and the subharmonic oscillations at the point D for which

$$C = 100 \,\mu\text{F} \quad \text{and} \quad V = 40 \,\text{volts}.$$

We shall now perform the experiments with this system.   As mentioned in Section 20 (a), we again prescribe the initial conditions with the initial charging voltage V_{C0} across the condenser and the phase angle θ_0 of the applied voltage at which it is impressed on the circuit.

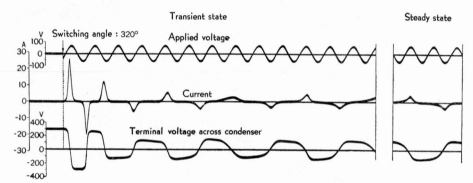

Fig. 22.2.   Oscillation leading to the subharmonic oscillation of order 1/3.

The oscillogram in Fig. 22.2 shows the transient state of an oscillation which gives rise to the subharmonic oscillation of order 1/3 in the steady state, in which the initial conditions are prescribed by

$$V_{C0} = 312 \,\text{volts} \quad \text{and} \quad \theta_0 = 320°.$$

Since the initial charging voltage is comparatively high, the transient oscillation at first has a higher frequency than in the steady state.   In order to compare this more clearly with the preceding analysis, we measure the flux density in the core and the phase angle of the applied voltage at every instant the oscillating current has an extreme value, and these are plotted in polar coordinates as illustrated in Fig. 22.3.*   The trajectories in the figure correspond to the integral curves in the shaded regions of Fig. 21.1, and we see that these trajectories spiral to the ultimate points with the increase of time.

---

* As long as the core loss is negligible, the exciting current and the resulting magnetic flux are considered to be in phase.   Therefore, the flux density has an extreme value at the phase angle mentioned above.

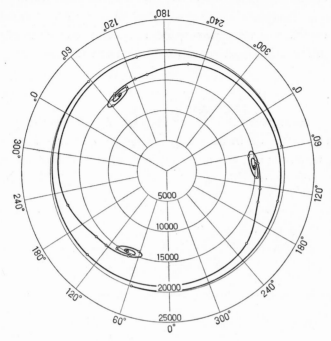

Fig. 22.3. Polar diagram showing the relationship between flux density and phase angle of applied voltage.

Radial scale: flux density (crest value in gauss) Angular scale: phase angle of applied voltage

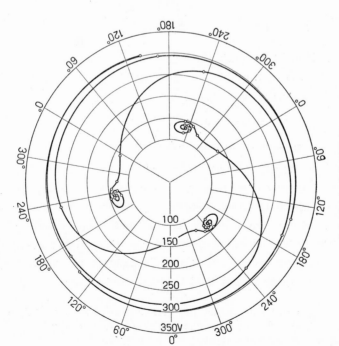

Fig. 22.4. Polar diagram showing the relationship between condenser voltage and phase angle of applied voltage.

Radial scale: voltage across condenser (crest value) Angular scale: phase angle of applied voltage

Similarly, the crest values of the condenser voltage and the corresponding phase angles of the applied voltage are plotted in Fig. 22.4. Since the oscillating current becomes zero at the instant the condenser is charged up to the crest voltage (see Fig. 22.2), subharmonic oscillation should take place if we start the oscillation with these crest voltages and phase angles as the initial

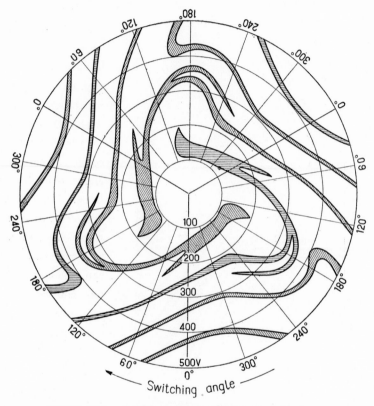

Radial scale: initial charging voltage across condenser

Fig. 22.5. Regions of initial conditions which lead to the subharmonic oscillation of order 1/3.

conditions, *viz.*, V_{C0} and θ_0, respectively. Hence, the points in Fig. 22.4 are the ones that prescribe the initial conditions giving rise to the subharmonic oscillation. By making use of the electronic synchronous switch as explained in Section 20 (a) (see also Appendix VI), we further determine (by varying the initial conditions V_{C0} and θ_0) the regions of initial conditions which lead either to the non-resonant state or to the subharmonic response. The experimental result is shown in Fig. 22.5, where the shaded regions are those which lead to the subharmonic response and the unshaded region to the non-resonant state. The figure is thus in good agreement with the theoretical result given in the preceding section (see Fig. 21.1).*

(b) Regions of initial conditions for a system in which all three types of periodic oscillation (*viz.*, the non-resonant, the resonant, and the subharmonic oscillations) are sustained

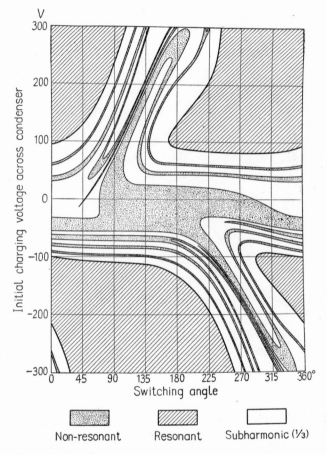

Fig. 22.6. Regions of initial conditions which lead to the different types of periodic oscillation.

It is clear from Fig. 22.1 that these three types of oscillation may be sustained when the applied voltage and the capacitance are given within the region common to both the shaded regions, one by full lines and the other by dotted lines. Figure 22.6 shows the result of an experiment obtained under such a condition. Although the theoretical analysis has not yet been accomplished,† it may be expected, by analogy with Figs. 20.2 and 22.5, that the regions of subharmonic oscillation are contracted by the appearance of the regions of resonant oscillation and distributed in narrower bands which are very close to one another.

---

* As noticed previously in Section 20 (a), the iron core was premagnetized (prior to each measurement) in a certain direction by forcing an ample direct current through the secondary winding on the core.

† The geometrical method of analysis applied in Section 21 fails in studying the case in which more than two states of periodic solution are sustained corresponding to the different values of the initial conditions.

APPENDIX I

EXPANSIONS OF THE MATHIEU FUNCTIONS

Mathieu's equation (3.1) (see Section 3.1 in the text) has the periodic solutions of period π or 2π corresponding to the characteristic numbers of a for a given q. Following Mathieu [22, 44] and Whittaker [36, 53], these periodic solutions, i.e., the Mathieu functions, are developed into power series of q when $|q|$ is small. Thus we write down some expansions in what follows.

First, for $ce_0(\tau, q)$, we have

$$ce_0(\tau, q) = 1 + 4q \cos 2\tau + 2q^2 \cos 4\tau + q^3 \left(-28 \cos 2\tau + \frac{4}{9} \cos 6\tau \right)$$

$$+ q^4 \left(-\frac{160}{9} \cos 4\tau + \frac{1}{18} \cos 8\tau \right) + \cdots,$$

for which the associated characteristic number is given by

$$a_{c0} = -32q^2 + 224q^4 - \frac{2^{10} \cdot 29}{9} q^6 + \cdots.$$

Similarly, for other Mathieu functions, we have

$$ce_1(\tau, q) = \cos \tau + q \cos 3\tau + q^2 \left(-\cos 3\tau + \frac{1}{3} \cos 5\tau \right)$$

$$+ q^3 \left(\frac{1}{3} \cos 3\tau - \frac{4}{9} \cos 5\tau + \frac{1}{18} \cos 7\tau \right)$$

$$+ q^4 \left(\frac{11}{9} \cos 3\tau + \frac{1}{6} \cos 5\tau - \frac{1}{12} \cos 7\tau + \frac{1}{180} \cos 9\tau \right) + \cdots,$$

$$se_1(\tau, q) = \sin \tau + q \sin 3\tau + q^2 \left(\sin 3\tau + \frac{1}{3} \sin 5\tau \right)$$

$$+ q^3 \left(\frac{1}{3} \sin 3\tau + \frac{4}{9} \sin 5\tau + \frac{1}{18} \sin 7\tau \right)$$

$$+ q^4 \left(-\frac{11}{9} \sin 3\tau + \frac{1}{6} \sin 5\tau + \frac{1}{12} \sin 7\tau + \frac{1}{180} \sin 9\tau \right) + \cdots,$$

$$ce_2(\tau, q) = \cos 2\tau + q \left(-2 + \frac{2}{3} \cos 4\tau \right) + \frac{1}{6} q^2 \cos 6\tau$$

125

$$+ q^3 \left(\frac{40}{3} + \frac{43}{27} \cos 4\tau + \frac{1}{45} \cos 8\tau \right)$$

$$+ q^4 \left(\frac{293}{540} \cos 6\tau + \frac{1}{540} \cos 10\tau \right) + \cdots ,$$

$$se_2(\tau, q) = \sin 2\tau + \frac{2}{3} q \sin 4\tau + \frac{1}{6} q^2 \sin 6\tau - q^3 \left(\frac{5}{27} \sin 4\tau - \frac{1}{45} \sin 8\tau \right)$$

$$+ q^4 \left(-\frac{37}{540} \sin 6\tau + \frac{1}{540} \sin 10\tau \right) + \cdots ,$$

$$ce_3(\tau, q) = \cos 3\tau - q \left(\cos \tau - \frac{1}{2} \cos 5\tau \right) + q^2 \left(\cos \tau + \frac{1}{10} \cos 7\tau \right)$$

$$- q^3 \left(\frac{1}{2} \cos \tau - \frac{7}{40} \cos 5\tau - \frac{1}{90} \cos 9\tau \right)$$

$$+ q^4 \left(- \cos \tau - \frac{1}{4} \cos 5\tau + \frac{17}{360} \cos 7\tau + \frac{1}{1260} \cos 11\tau \right) + \cdots ,$$

$$se_3(\tau, q) = \sin 3\tau - q \left(\sin \tau - \frac{1}{2} \sin 5\tau \right) + q^2 \left(- \sin \tau + \frac{1}{10} \sin 7\tau \right)$$

$$- q^3 \left(\frac{1}{2} \sin \tau - \frac{7}{40} \sin 5\tau - \frac{1}{90} \sin 9\tau \right)$$

$$+ q^4 \left(\sin \tau + \frac{1}{4} \sin 5\tau + \frac{17}{360} \sin 7\tau + \frac{1}{1260} \sin 11\tau \right) + \cdots .$$

The characteristic numbers a_{cn} and a_{sn} associated, respectively, with the Mathieu functions $ce_n(\tau, q)$ and $se_n(\tau, q)$ were previously given by equations (3.5) in Section 3.2.

APPENDIX II

UNSTABLE SOLUTIONS OF HILL'S EQUATION

As mentioned in Section 5.1, the stability conditions (5.5) and (5.7) were calculated to a first approximation since the characteristic exponent μ was determined by equation (4.7). However, a closer approximation of the characteristic exponent will be necessary in case the stability condition of a higher order approximation is desired. Therefore, proceeding in the same manner as in the case of Mathieu's equation (see Section 3.3), we shall calculate the unstable solutions of Hill's equation (with $\nu = 1$ to 4)

$$\frac{d^2x}{d\tau^2} + \left[\theta_0 + 2 \sum_{\nu=1}^{4} \theta_\nu \cos 2\nu\tau \right] x = 0 . \tag{II.1}$$

Following Whittaker [36; 53, p. 424], let the general solution of (II.1) be

$$x = c_1 e^{\mu\tau} \phi(\tau, \sigma) + c_2 e^{-\mu\tau} \phi(\tau, -\sigma), \tag{II.2}$$

where c_1 and c_2 are arbitrary constants. Then, we obtain the expansions for μ and θ_0 as follows.*

(a) For the unbounded solution associated with the first unstable region:†
   The characteristic exponent μ is given by

$$\left. \begin{aligned} \mu &= \frac{1}{2} \theta_1 \sin 2\sigma + \frac{1}{8} \theta_1\theta_2 \sin 2\sigma + \frac{1}{24} \theta_2\theta_3 \sin 2\sigma - \frac{3}{128} \theta_1^3 \sin 2\sigma \\ &\quad + \frac{1}{128} \theta_1^2\theta_2 \sin 4\sigma + \frac{5}{384} \theta_1^2\theta_3 \sin 2\sigma + \frac{7}{288} \theta_1\theta_2^2 \sin 2\sigma \\ &\quad + \frac{17}{4608} \theta_1\theta_3^2 \sin 2\sigma + \frac{1}{96} \theta_2^2\theta_3 \sin 2\sigma + \frac{1}{1152} \theta_1\theta_2\theta_3 \sin 4\sigma + \cdots , \end{aligned} \right\} \tag{II.3}$$

in which the parameter σ is to be determined by

$$\left. \begin{aligned} \theta_0 &= 1 + \theta_1 \cos 2\sigma + \left(-\frac{1}{4} + \frac{1}{8} \cos 4\sigma \right) \theta_1^2 - \frac{1}{6} \theta_2^2 - \frac{1}{16} \theta_3^2 + \frac{1}{4} \theta_1\theta_2 \cos 2\sigma \\ &\quad + \frac{1}{12} \theta_2\theta_3 \cos 2\sigma - \frac{1}{64} \theta_1^3 \cos 2\sigma + \left(-\frac{11}{192} + \frac{5}{64} \cos 4\sigma \right) \theta_1^2\theta_2 \end{aligned} \right\} \tag{II.4}$$

---

* The computation is carried out up to terms of the third degree in θ's.

† The parameter θ_4 is excluded only in this case.

127

$$+ \frac{5}{192}\,\theta_1^2\theta_3\cos 2\sigma - \frac{1}{144}\,\theta_1\theta_2^2\cos 2\sigma - \frac{1}{2304}\,\theta_1\theta_3^2\cos 2\sigma$$

$$+ \frac{1}{48}\,\theta_2^2\theta_3\cos 2\sigma + \left(-\frac{13}{192} + \frac{13}{576}\cos 4\sigma\right)\theta_1\theta_2\theta_3 + \cdots .$$

(b) For the unbounded solution associated with the second unstable region:
Similar to the preceding case, the expansions for μ and θ_0 are given by

$$\begin{aligned}
\mu = {} & \frac{1}{4}\,\theta_2\sin 2\sigma - \frac{1}{16}\,\theta_1^2\sin 2\sigma + \frac{1}{24}\,\theta_1\theta_3\sin 2\sigma + \frac{1}{64}\,\theta_2\theta_4\sin 2\sigma \\[4pt]
& - \frac{3}{4096}\,\theta_2^3\sin 2\sigma + \left(-\frac{1}{72}\sin 2\sigma + \frac{1}{128}\sin 4\sigma\right)\theta_1^2\theta_2 + \frac{7}{2304}\,\theta_1^2\theta_4\sin 2\sigma \\[4pt]
& + \frac{1}{4096}\,\theta_2^2\theta_4\sin 4\sigma + \frac{7}{1800}\,\theta_2\theta_3^2\sin 2\sigma + \frac{7}{9216}\,\theta_2\theta_4^2\sin 2\sigma \\[4pt]
& + \frac{5}{2304}\,\theta_3^2\theta_4\sin 2\sigma + \left(-\frac{5}{384}\sin 2\sigma + \frac{1}{576}\sin 4\sigma\right)\theta_1\theta_2\theta_3 \\[4pt]
& - \frac{11}{1920}\,\theta_1\theta_3\theta_4\sin 2\sigma + \cdots ,
\end{aligned} \qquad \text{(II.5)}$$

$$\begin{aligned}
\theta_0 = {} & 4 + \theta_2\cos 2\sigma + \left(\frac{1}{6} - \frac{1}{4}\cos 2\sigma\right)\theta_1^2 + \left(-\frac{1}{16} + \frac{1}{32}\cos 4\sigma\right)\theta_2^2 - \frac{1}{10}\,\theta_3^2 \\[4pt]
& - \frac{1}{24}\,\theta_4^2 + \frac{1}{6}\,\theta_1\theta_3\cos 2\sigma + \frac{1}{16}\,\theta_2\theta_4\cos 2\sigma - \frac{1}{1024}\,\theta_2^3\cos 2\sigma \\[4pt]
& + \left(\frac{1}{12} - \frac{1}{9}\cos 2\sigma + \frac{1}{64}\cos 4\sigma\right)\theta_1^2\theta_2 + \frac{7}{576}\,\theta_1^2\theta_4\cos 2\sigma \\[4pt]
& + \left(-\frac{11}{3072} + \frac{5}{1024}\cos 4\sigma\right)\theta_2^2\theta_4 - \frac{1}{225}\,\theta_2\theta_3^2\cos 2\sigma - \frac{1}{2304}\,\theta_2\theta_4^2\cos 2\sigma \\[4pt]
& + \frac{5}{576}\,\theta_3^2\theta_4\cos 2\sigma + \left(\frac{1}{20} - \frac{5}{96}\cos 2\sigma + \frac{5}{288}\cos 4\sigma\right)\theta_1\theta_2\theta_3 \\[4pt]
& + \left(\frac{1}{360} - \frac{11}{480}\cos 2\sigma\right)\theta_1\theta_3\theta_4 + \cdots .
\end{aligned} \qquad \text{(II.6)}$$

(c) For the unbounded solution associated with the third unstable region:

$$\begin{aligned}
\mu = {} & \frac{1}{6}\,\theta_3\sin 2\sigma - \frac{1}{24}\,\theta_1\theta_2\sin 2\sigma + \frac{1}{48}\,\theta_1\theta_4\sin 2\sigma + \frac{1}{384}\,\theta_1^3\sin 2\sigma \\[4pt]
& - \frac{1}{10368}\,\theta_3^3\sin 2\sigma - \frac{7}{1536}\,\theta_1^2\theta_3\sin 2\sigma - \frac{1}{2400}\,\theta_2^2\theta_3\sin 2\sigma \\[4pt]
& + \frac{23}{18816}\,\theta_3\theta_4^2\sin 2\sigma + \frac{1}{384}\,\theta_1\theta_2\theta_3\sin 4\sigma - \frac{1}{320}\,\theta_1\theta_2\theta_4\sin 2\sigma \\[4pt]
& + \frac{1}{1536}\,\theta_1\theta_3\theta_4\sin 4\sigma - \frac{5}{1728}\,\theta_2\theta_3\theta_4\sin 2\sigma + \cdots ,
\end{aligned} \qquad \text{(II.7)}$$

$$
\left.
\begin{aligned}
\theta_0 &= 9 + \theta_3 \cos 2\sigma + \frac{1}{16}\,\theta_1^2 + \frac{1}{10}\,\theta_2^2 + \left(-\frac{1}{36} + \frac{1}{72}\cos 4\sigma\right)\theta_3^2 - \frac{1}{14}\,\theta_4^2 \\[2mm]
&\quad - \frac{1}{4}\,\theta_1\theta_2 \cos 2\sigma + \frac{1}{8}\,\theta_1\theta_4 \cos 2\sigma + \frac{1}{64}\,\theta_1^3 \cos 2\sigma - \frac{1}{5184}\,\theta_3^3 \cos 2\sigma \\[2mm]
&\quad - \frac{3}{160}\,\theta_1^2\theta_2 - \frac{9}{256}\,\theta_1^2\theta_3 \cos 2\sigma - \frac{9}{400}\,\theta_2^2\theta_3 \cos 2\sigma + \frac{3}{140}\,\theta_2^2\theta_4 \\[2mm]
&\quad - \frac{9}{3136}\,\theta_3\theta_4^2 \cos 2\sigma + \left(\frac{121}{2880} + \frac{5}{576}\cos 4\sigma\right)\theta_1\theta_2\theta_3 \\[2mm]
&\quad - \frac{3}{160}\,\theta_1\theta_2\theta_4 \cos 2\sigma + \left(\frac{293}{16128} + \frac{17}{2304}\cos 4\sigma\right)\theta_1\theta_3\theta_4 \\[2mm]
&\quad - \frac{5}{288}\,\theta_2\theta_3\theta_4 \cos 2\sigma + \cdots .
\end{aligned}
\right\} \quad (\text{II}.8)
$$

The periodic functions $\phi(\tau, \sigma)$ and $\phi(\tau, -\sigma)$ in equation (II.2) are obtained at the same time for the respective unstable regions. They have, however, no direct connection with the stability criterion, so that the full details of the expansions of these periodic functions are omitted here.*

-----

* It is noticed that the expansions of the periodic functions up to terms of the second degree in θ's may be obtained by putting $\varepsilon_\nu = 0$ in Appendix III which follows.

APPENDIX III

UNSTABLE SOLUTIONS FOR THE EXTENDED FORM OF HILL'S EQUATION

We shall here calculate closely the unstable solution of equation (4.11) in Section 4.2. Considering the alternative form (with $\nu = 1$ to 4)

$$\frac{d^2x}{d\tau^2} + \left[\theta_0 + 2 \sum_{\nu=1}^{4} \theta_\nu \cos\left(2\nu\tau - \varepsilon_\nu\right) \right] x = 0, \tag{III.1}$$

the general solution will be expressed by

$$x = c_1 e^{\mu\tau} \phi\left(\tau, \sigma_1\right) + c_2 e^{-\mu\tau} \phi\left(\tau, \sigma_2\right), \tag{III.2}$$

in which c_1, c_2 are arbitrary constants, and the parameters σ_1, σ_2 are determined by the expansions of θ_0 in what follows.

(a) For the unbounded solution associated with the first unstable region:

$$\left.\begin{aligned}
\mu = {} & \frac{1}{2}\,\theta_1 \sin 2\sigma + \frac{1}{8}\,\theta_1\theta_2 \sin\left(2\sigma + 2\varepsilon_1 - \varepsilon_2\right) + \frac{1}{24}\,\theta_2\theta_3 \sin\left(2\sigma + \varepsilon_1 + \varepsilon_2 - \varepsilon_3\right) \\
& + \frac{1}{48}\,\theta_3\theta_4 \sin\left(2\sigma + \varepsilon_1 + \varepsilon_3 - \varepsilon_4\right) + \cdots,
\end{aligned}\right\} \tag{III.3}$$

$$\left.\begin{aligned}
\theta_0 = {} & 1 + \theta_1 \cos 2\sigma + \left(-\frac{1}{4} + \frac{1}{8} \cos 4\sigma \right) \theta_1^2 - \frac{1}{6}\,\theta_2^2 - \frac{1}{16}\,\theta_3^2 - \frac{1}{30}\,\theta_4^2 \\
& + \frac{1}{4}\,\theta_1\theta_2 \cos\left(2\sigma + 2\varepsilon_1 - \varepsilon_2\right) + \frac{1}{12}\,\theta_2\theta_3 \cos\left(2\sigma + \varepsilon_1 + \varepsilon_2 - \varepsilon_3\right) \\
& + \frac{1}{24}\,\theta_3\theta_4 \cos\left(2\sigma + \varepsilon_1 + \varepsilon_3 - \varepsilon_4\right) + \cdots,*
\end{aligned}\right\} \tag{III.4}$$

$$\left.\begin{aligned}
\phi\left(\tau, \sigma\right) = {} & \sin\left(\tau - \frac{\varepsilon_1}{2} - \sigma\right) + A_1\theta_1 + A_2\theta_2 + A_3\theta_3 + A_4\theta_4 + B_1\theta_1^2 + B_2\theta_2^2 + B_3\theta_3^2 + B_4\theta_4^2 \\
& + B_{12}\theta_1\theta_2 + B_{13}\theta_1\theta_3 + B_{14}\theta_1\theta_4 + B_{23}\theta_2\theta_3 + B_{24}\theta_2\theta_4 + B_{34}\theta_3\theta_4 + \cdots,
\end{aligned}\right\} \tag{III.5}$$

where

$$A_1 = \frac{1}{8} \sin\left(3\tau - \frac{3}{2}\,\varepsilon_1 - \sigma\right),$$

---

* Solving for σ, we obtain two principal values σ_1 and σ_2.

$$A_2 = -\frac{1}{8}\cos 2\sigma \cdot \sin\left(3\tau + \frac{\varepsilon_1}{2} - \varepsilon_2 - \sigma\right) - \frac{1}{8}\sin 2\sigma \cdot \cos\left(3\tau + \frac{\varepsilon_1}{2} - \varepsilon_2 - \sigma\right)$$

$$+\frac{1}{24}\sin\left(5\tau - \frac{\varepsilon_1}{2} - \varepsilon_2 - \sigma\right),$$

$$A_3 = -\frac{1}{24}\cos 2\sigma \cdot \sin\left(5\tau + \frac{\varepsilon_1}{2} - \varepsilon_3 - \sigma\right) - \frac{1}{24}\sin 2\sigma \cdot \cos\left(5\tau + \frac{\varepsilon_1}{2} - \varepsilon_3 - \sigma\right)$$

$$+\frac{1}{48}\sin\left(7\tau - \frac{\varepsilon_1}{2} - \varepsilon_3 - \sigma\right),$$

$$A_4 = -\frac{1}{48}\cos 2\sigma \cdot \sin\left(7\tau + \frac{\varepsilon_1}{2} - \varepsilon_4 - \sigma\right) - \frac{1}{48}\sin 2\sigma \cdot \cos\left(7\tau + \frac{\varepsilon_1}{2} - \varepsilon_4 - \sigma\right)$$

$$+\frac{1}{80}\sin\left(9\tau - \frac{\varepsilon_1}{2} - \varepsilon_4 - \sigma\right),$$

$$B_1 = \frac{1}{64}\cos 2\sigma \cdot \sin\left(3\tau - \frac{3}{2}\varepsilon_1 - \sigma\right) + \frac{3}{64}\sin 2\sigma \cdot \cos\left(3\tau - \frac{3}{2}\varepsilon_1 - \sigma\right)$$

$$+\frac{1}{192}\sin\left(5\tau - \frac{5}{2}\varepsilon_1 - \sigma\right),$$

$$B_2 = -\frac{1}{384}\cos 2\sigma \cdot \sin\left(7\tau + \frac{\varepsilon_1}{2} - 2\varepsilon_2 - \sigma\right) - \frac{1}{384}\sin 2\sigma \cdot \cos\left(7\tau + \frac{\varepsilon_1}{2} - 2\varepsilon_2 - \sigma\right)$$

$$+\frac{1}{1920}\sin\left(9\tau - \frac{\varepsilon_1}{2} - 2\varepsilon_2 - \sigma\right),$$

$$B_3 = -\frac{1}{2880}\cos 2\sigma \cdot \sin\left(11\tau + \frac{\varepsilon_1}{2} - 2\varepsilon_3 - \sigma\right) - \frac{1}{2880}\sin 2\sigma \cdot \cos\left(11\tau + \frac{\varepsilon_1}{2} - 2\varepsilon_3 - \sigma\right)$$

$$+\frac{1}{8064}\sin\left(13\tau - \frac{\varepsilon_1}{2} - 2\varepsilon_3 - \sigma\right),$$

$$B_4 = -\frac{1}{10752}\cos 2\sigma \cdot \sin\left(15\tau + \frac{\varepsilon_1}{2} - 2\varepsilon_4 - \sigma\right) - \frac{1}{10752}\sin 2\sigma \cdot \cos\left(15\tau + \frac{\varepsilon_1}{2} - 2\varepsilon_4 - \sigma\right)$$

$$+\frac{1}{23040}\sin\left(17\tau - \frac{\varepsilon_1}{2} - 2\varepsilon_4 - \sigma\right),$$

$$B_{12} = \left(\frac{1}{48} - \frac{1}{32}\cos 4\sigma\right)\sin\left(3\tau + \frac{\varepsilon_1}{2} - \varepsilon_2 - \sigma\right) - \frac{1}{32}\sin 4\sigma \cdot \cos\left(3\tau + \frac{\varepsilon_1}{2} - \varepsilon_2 - \sigma\right)$$

$$-\frac{1}{288}\cos 2\sigma \cdot \sin\left(5\tau - \frac{\varepsilon_1}{2} - \varepsilon_2 - \sigma\right) + \frac{1}{288}\sin 2\sigma \cdot \cos\left(5\tau - \frac{\varepsilon_1}{2} - \varepsilon_2 - \sigma\right)$$

$$+\frac{1}{288}\sin\left(7\tau - \frac{3}{2}\varepsilon_1 - \varepsilon_2 - \sigma\right),$$

$$B_{13} = -\frac{1}{48}\cos 2\sigma \cdot \sin\left(3\tau + \frac{3}{2}\varepsilon_1 - \varepsilon_3 - \sigma\right) - \frac{1}{48}\sin 2\sigma \cdot \cos\left(3\tau + \frac{3}{2}\varepsilon_1 - \varepsilon_3 - \sigma\right)$$

$$+\left(\frac{5}{1152} - \frac{1}{192}\cos 4\sigma\right)\sin\left(5\tau + \frac{\varepsilon_1}{2} - \varepsilon_3 - \sigma\right) - \frac{1}{192}\sin 4\sigma \cdot \cos\left(5\tau + \frac{\varepsilon_1}{2} - \varepsilon_3 - \sigma\right)$$

$$-\frac{1}{2304}\cos 2\sigma \cdot \sin\left(7\tau - \frac{\varepsilon_1}{2} - \varepsilon_3 - \sigma\right) + \frac{5}{2304}\sin 2\sigma \cdot \cos\left(7\tau - \frac{\varepsilon_1}{2} - \varepsilon_3 - \sigma\right)$$

$$+ \frac{7}{3840} \sin \left(9\tau - \frac{3}{2}\,\varepsilon_1 - \varepsilon_3 - \sigma\right),$$

$$B_{14} = -\frac{7}{1152} \cos 2\sigma \cdot \sin \left(5\tau + \frac{3}{2}\,\varepsilon_1 - \varepsilon_4 - \sigma\right) - \frac{7}{1152} \sin 2\sigma \cdot \cos \left(5\tau + \frac{3}{2}\,\varepsilon_1 - \varepsilon_4 - \sigma\right)$$

$$+ \left(\frac{1}{640} - \frac{1}{576} \cos 4\sigma\right) \sin \left(7\tau + \frac{\varepsilon_1}{2} - \varepsilon_4 - \sigma\right) - \frac{1}{576} \sin 4\sigma \cdot \cos \left(7\tau + \frac{\varepsilon_1}{2} - \varepsilon_4 - \sigma\right)$$

$$- \frac{1}{9600} \cos 2\sigma \cdot \sin \left(9\tau - \frac{\varepsilon_1}{2} - \varepsilon_4 - \sigma\right) + \frac{11}{9600} \sin 2\sigma \cdot \cos \left(9\tau - \frac{\varepsilon_1}{2} - \varepsilon_4 - \sigma\right)$$

$$+ \frac{11}{9600} \sin \left(11\tau - \frac{3}{2}\,\varepsilon_1 - \varepsilon_4 - \sigma\right),$$

$$B_{23} = \frac{7}{384} \sin \left(3\tau - \frac{\varepsilon_1}{2} + \varepsilon_2 - \varepsilon_3 - \sigma\right) - \frac{1}{480} \cos 2\sigma \cdot \sin \left(9\tau + \frac{\varepsilon_1}{2} - \varepsilon_2 - \varepsilon_3 - \sigma\right)$$

$$- \frac{1}{480} \sin 2\sigma \cdot \cos \left(9\tau + \frac{\varepsilon_1}{2} - \varepsilon_2 - \varepsilon_3 - \sigma\right) + \frac{1}{1920} \sin \left(11\tau - \frac{\varepsilon_1}{2} - \varepsilon_2 - \varepsilon_3 - \sigma\right),$$

$$B_{24} = -\frac{1}{128} \cos 2\sigma \cdot \sin \left(3\tau + \frac{\varepsilon_1}{2} + \varepsilon_2 - \varepsilon_4 - \sigma\right) - \frac{1}{128} \sin 2\sigma \cdot \cos \left(3\tau + \frac{\varepsilon_1}{2} + \varepsilon_2 - \varepsilon_4 - \sigma\right)$$

$$+ \frac{11}{1920} \sin \left(5\tau - \frac{\varepsilon_1}{2} + \varepsilon_2 - \varepsilon_4 - \sigma\right) - \frac{7}{5760} \cos 2\sigma \cdot \sin \left(11\tau + \frac{\varepsilon_1}{2} - \varepsilon_2 - \varepsilon_4 - \sigma\right)$$

$$- \frac{7}{5760} \sin 2\sigma \cdot \cos \left(11\tau + \frac{\varepsilon_1}{2} - \varepsilon_2 - \varepsilon_4 - \sigma\right) + \frac{13}{40320} \sin \left(13\tau - \frac{\varepsilon_1}{2} - \varepsilon_2 - \varepsilon_4 - \sigma\right),$$

$$B_{34} = \frac{13}{1920} \sin \left(3\tau - \frac{\varepsilon_1}{2} + \varepsilon_3 - \varepsilon_4 - \sigma\right) - \frac{1}{2688} \cos 2\sigma \cdot \sin \left(13\tau + \frac{\varepsilon_1}{2} - \varepsilon_3 - \varepsilon_4 - \sigma\right)$$

$$- \frac{1}{2688} \sin 2\sigma \cdot \cos \left(13\tau + \frac{\varepsilon_1}{2} - \varepsilon_3 - \varepsilon_4 - \sigma\right) + \frac{1}{6720} \sin \left(15\tau - \frac{\varepsilon_1}{2} - \varepsilon_3 - \varepsilon_4 - \sigma\right).$$

(b) For the unbounded solution associated with the second unstable region:

$$\mu = \frac{1}{4}\,\theta_2 \sin 2\sigma - \frac{1}{16}\,\theta_1^2 \sin (2\sigma - 2\varepsilon_1 + \varepsilon_2) + \frac{1}{24}\,\theta_1\theta_3 \sin (2\sigma + \varepsilon_1 + \varepsilon_2 - \varepsilon_3)$$

$$+ \frac{1}{64}\,\theta_2\theta_4 \sin (2\sigma + 2\varepsilon_2 - \varepsilon_4) + \cdots, \qquad\qquad (\text{III.6})$$

$$\theta_0 = 4 + \theta_2 \cos 2\sigma + \left[\frac{1}{6} - \frac{1}{4} \cos (2\sigma - 2\varepsilon_1 + \varepsilon_2)\right]\theta_1^2 + \left(-\frac{1}{16} + \frac{1}{32} \cos 4\sigma\right)\theta_2^2$$

$$- \frac{1}{10}\,\theta_3^2 - \frac{1}{24}\,\theta_4^2 + \frac{1}{6}\,\theta_1\theta_3 \cos (2\sigma + \varepsilon_1 + \varepsilon_2 - \varepsilon_3) + \frac{1}{16}\,\theta_2\theta_4 \cos (2\sigma + 2\varepsilon_2$$

$$- \varepsilon_4) + \cdots, \qquad\qquad (\text{III.7})$$

$$\phi(\tau, \sigma) = \sin \left(2\tau - \frac{\varepsilon_2}{2} - \sigma\right) + A_1\theta_1 + A_2\theta_2 + A_3\theta_3 + A_4\theta_4 + B_1\theta_1^2 + B_2\theta_2^2 + B_3\theta_3^2$$

$$+ B_4\theta_4^2 + B_{12}\theta_1\theta_2 + B_{13}\theta_1\theta_3 + B_{14}\theta_1\theta_4 + B_{23}\theta_2\theta_3 + B_{24}\theta_2\theta_4 + B_{34}\theta_3\theta_4 + \cdots, \qquad (\text{III.8})$$

where

$$A_1 = -\frac{1}{4}\sin\left(\varepsilon_1 - \frac{\varepsilon_2}{2} - \sigma\right) + \frac{1}{12}\sin\left(4\tau - \varepsilon_1 - \frac{\varepsilon_2}{2} - \sigma\right),$$

$$A_2 = \frac{1}{32}\sin\left(6\tau - \frac{3}{2}\varepsilon_2 - \sigma\right),$$

$$A_3 = -\frac{1}{12}\cos 2\sigma\cdot\sin\left(4\tau + \frac{\varepsilon_2}{2} - \varepsilon_3 - \sigma\right) - \frac{1}{12}\sin 2\sigma\cdot\cos\left(4\tau + \frac{\varepsilon_2}{2} - \varepsilon_3 - \sigma\right)$$
$$+ \frac{1}{60}\sin\left(8\tau - \frac{\varepsilon_2}{2} - \varepsilon_3 - \sigma\right),$$

$$A_4 = -\frac{1}{32}\cos 2\sigma\cdot\sin\left(6\tau + \frac{\varepsilon_2}{2} - \varepsilon_4 - \sigma\right) - \frac{1}{32}\sin 2\sigma\cdot\cos\left(6\tau + \frac{\varepsilon_2}{2} - \varepsilon_4 - \sigma\right)$$
$$+ \frac{1}{96}\sin\left(10\tau - \frac{\varepsilon_2}{2} - \varepsilon_4 - \sigma\right),$$

$$B_1 = \frac{1}{384}\sin\left(6\tau - 2\varepsilon_1 - \frac{\varepsilon_2}{2} - \sigma\right),$$

$$B_2 = \frac{1}{1024}\cos 2\sigma\cdot\sin\left(6\tau - \frac{3}{2}\varepsilon_2 - \sigma\right) + \frac{3}{1024}\sin 2\sigma\cdot\cos\left(6\tau - \frac{3}{2}\varepsilon_2 - \sigma\right)$$
$$+ \frac{1}{3072}\sin\left(10\tau - \frac{5}{2}\varepsilon_2 - \sigma\right),$$

$$B_3 = -\frac{1}{1152}\cos 2\sigma\cdot\sin\left(10\tau + \frac{\varepsilon_2}{2} - 2\varepsilon_3 - \sigma\right) - \frac{1}{1152}\sin 2\sigma\cdot\cos\left(10\tau + \frac{\varepsilon_2}{2} - 2\varepsilon_3 - \sigma\right)$$
$$+ \frac{1}{11520}\sin\left(14\tau - \frac{\varepsilon_2}{2} - 2\varepsilon_3 - \sigma\right),$$

$$B_4 = -\frac{1}{6144}\cos 2\sigma\cdot\sin\left(14\tau + \frac{\varepsilon_2}{2} - 2\varepsilon_4 - \sigma\right) - \frac{1}{6144}\sin 2\sigma\cdot\cos\left(14\tau + \frac{\varepsilon_2}{2} - 2\varepsilon_4 - \sigma\right)$$
$$+ \frac{1}{30720}\sin\left(18\tau - \frac{\varepsilon_2}{2} - 2\varepsilon_4 - \sigma\right),$$

$$B_{12} = \frac{5}{96}\sin\left(\sigma + \varepsilon_1 - \frac{\varepsilon_2}{2}\right) - \frac{1}{32}\sin\left(3\sigma - \varepsilon_1 + \frac{\varepsilon_2}{2}\right) - \frac{7}{384}\sin\left(4\tau + \varepsilon_1 - \frac{3}{2}\varepsilon_2 - \sigma\right)$$
$$+ \frac{1}{36}\cos 2\sigma\cdot\sin\left(4\tau - \varepsilon_1 - \frac{\varepsilon_2}{2} - \sigma\right) + \frac{5}{144}\sin 2\sigma\cdot\cos\left(4\tau - \varepsilon_1 - \frac{\varepsilon_2}{2} - \sigma\right)$$
$$+ \frac{11}{5760}\sin\left(8\tau - \varepsilon_1 - \frac{3}{2}\varepsilon_2 - \sigma\right),$$

$$B_{13} = -\frac{7}{960}\sin\left(6\tau + \varepsilon_1 - \frac{\varepsilon_2}{2} - \varepsilon_3 - \sigma\right) + \frac{1}{192}\cos 2\sigma\cdot\sin\left(6\tau - \varepsilon_1 + \frac{\varepsilon_2}{2} - \varepsilon_3 - \sigma\right)$$
$$+ \frac{1}{192}\sin 2\sigma\cdot\cos\left(6\tau - \varepsilon_1 + \frac{\varepsilon_2}{2} - \varepsilon_3 - \sigma\right) + \frac{1}{960}\sin\left(10\tau - \varepsilon_1 - \frac{\varepsilon_2}{2} - \varepsilon_3 - \sigma\right),$$

$$B_{14} = -\frac{11}{1152}\cos 2\sigma\cdot\sin\left(4\tau + \varepsilon_1 + \frac{\varepsilon_2}{2} - \varepsilon_4 - \sigma\right) - \frac{11}{1152}\sin 2\sigma\cdot\cos\left(4\tau + \varepsilon_1 + \frac{\varepsilon_2}{2} - \varepsilon_4 - \sigma\right)$$

$$-\frac{23}{5760}\sin\left(8\tau+\varepsilon_1-\frac{\varepsilon_2}{2}-\varepsilon_4-\sigma\right)+\frac{7}{1920}\cos 2\sigma\cdot\sin\left(8\tau-\varepsilon_1+\frac{\varepsilon_2}{2}-\varepsilon_4-\sigma\right)$$

$$+\frac{7}{1920}\sin 2\sigma\cdot\cos\left(8\tau-\varepsilon_1+\frac{\varepsilon_2}{2}-\varepsilon_4-\sigma\right)+\frac{3}{4480}\sin\left(12\tau-\varepsilon_1-\frac{\varepsilon_2}{2}-\varepsilon_4-\sigma\right),$$

$$B_{23}=\frac{11}{384}\sin\left(\sigma+\frac{3}{2}\varepsilon_2-\varepsilon_3\right)+\left(\frac{7}{1440}-\frac{1}{96}\cos 4\sigma\right)\sin\left(4\tau+\frac{\varepsilon_2}{2}-\varepsilon_3-\sigma\right)$$

$$-\frac{1}{96}\sin 4\sigma\cdot\cos\left(4\tau+\frac{\varepsilon_2}{2}-\varepsilon_3-\sigma\right)-\frac{1}{900}\cos 2\sigma\cdot\sin\left(8\tau-\frac{\varepsilon_2}{2}-\varepsilon_3-\sigma\right)$$

$$-\frac{1}{3600}\sin 2\sigma\cdot\cos\left(8\tau-\frac{\varepsilon_2}{2}-\varepsilon_3-\sigma\right)+\frac{23}{67200}\sin\left(12\tau-\frac{3}{2}\varepsilon_2-\varepsilon_3-\sigma\right),$$

$$B_{24}=\left(\frac{1}{768}-\frac{1}{512}\cos 4\sigma\right)\sin\left(6\tau+\frac{\varepsilon_2}{2}-\varepsilon_4-\sigma\right)-\frac{1}{512}\sin 4\sigma\cdot\cos\left(6\tau+\frac{\varepsilon_2}{2}-\varepsilon_4-\sigma\right)$$

$$-\frac{1}{4608}\cos 2\sigma\cdot\sin\left(10\tau-\frac{\varepsilon_2}{2}-\varepsilon_4-\sigma\right)+\frac{1}{4608}\sin 2\sigma\cdot\cos\left(10\tau-\frac{\varepsilon_2}{2}-\varepsilon_4-\sigma\right)$$

$$+\frac{1}{4608}\sin\left(14\tau-\frac{3}{2}\varepsilon_2-\varepsilon_4-\sigma\right),$$

$$B_{34}=\frac{23}{1920}\sin\left(\sigma+\frac{\varepsilon_2}{2}+\varepsilon_3-\varepsilon_4\right)+\frac{1}{128}\sin\left(4\tau-\frac{\varepsilon_2}{2}+\varepsilon_3-\varepsilon_4-\sigma\right)-\frac{11}{13440}$$

$$\cos 2\sigma\cdot\sin\left(12\tau+\frac{\varepsilon_2}{2}-\varepsilon_3-\varepsilon_4-\sigma\right)-\frac{11}{13440}\sin 2\sigma\cdot\cos\left(12\tau+\frac{\varepsilon_2}{2}-\varepsilon_3-\varepsilon_4-\sigma\right)$$

$$+\frac{13}{120960}\sin\left(16\tau-\frac{\varepsilon_2}{2}-\varepsilon_3-\varepsilon_4-\sigma\right).$$

(c) For the unbounded solution associated with the third unstable region:

$$\mu=\frac{1}{6}\theta_3\sin 2\sigma-\frac{1}{24}\theta_1\theta_2\sin(2\sigma-\varepsilon_1-\varepsilon_2+\varepsilon_3)+\frac{1}{48}\theta_1\theta_4\sin(2\sigma+\varepsilon_1+\varepsilon_3$$
$$-\varepsilon_4)+\cdots,$$

$$\left.\right\}\quad\text{(III.9)}$$

$$\theta_0=9+\theta_3\cos 2\sigma+\frac{1}{16}\theta_1^2+\frac{1}{10}\theta_2^2+\left(-\frac{1}{36}+\frac{1}{72}\cos 4\sigma\right)\theta_3^2-\frac{1}{14}\theta_4^2$$
$$-\frac{1}{4}\theta_1\theta_2\cos(2\sigma-\varepsilon_1-\varepsilon_2+\varepsilon_3)+\frac{1}{8}\theta_1\theta_4\cos(2\sigma+\varepsilon_1+\varepsilon_3-\varepsilon_4)+\cdots,$$

$$\left.\right\}\quad\text{(III.10)}$$

$$\phi(\tau,\sigma)=\sin\left(3\tau-\frac{\varepsilon_3}{2}-\sigma\right)+A_1\theta_1+A_2\theta_2+A_3\theta_3+A_4\theta_4+B_1\theta_1^2+B_2\theta_2^2+B_3\theta_3^2$$
$$+B_4\theta_4^2+B_{12}\theta_1\theta_2+B_{13}\theta_1\theta_3+B_{14}\theta_1\theta_4+B_{23}\theta_2\theta_3+B_{24}\theta_2\theta_4+B_{34}\theta_3\theta_4+\cdots,$$

$$\left.\right\}\quad\text{(III.11)}$$

where

$$A_1=-\frac{1}{8}\sin\left(\tau+\varepsilon_1-\frac{\varepsilon_3}{2}-\sigma\right)+\frac{1}{16}\sin\left(5\tau-\varepsilon_1-\frac{\varepsilon_3}{2}-\sigma\right),$$

$$A_2 = \frac{1}{8}\cos 2\sigma \cdot \sin\left(\tau - \varepsilon_2 + \frac{\varepsilon_3}{2} - \sigma\right) + \frac{1}{8}\sin 2\sigma \cdot \cos\left(\tau - \varepsilon_2 + \frac{\varepsilon_3}{2} - \sigma\right)$$

$$+ \frac{1}{40}\sin\left(7\tau - \varepsilon_2 - \frac{\varepsilon_3}{2} - \sigma\right),$$

$$A_3 = \frac{1}{72}\sin\left(9\tau - \frac{3}{2}\varepsilon_3 - \sigma\right),$$

$$A_4 = -\frac{1}{16}\cos 2\sigma \cdot \sin\left(5\tau + \frac{\varepsilon_3}{2} - \varepsilon_4 - \sigma\right) - \frac{1}{16}\sin 2\sigma \cdot \cos\left(5\tau + \frac{\varepsilon_3}{2} - \varepsilon_4 - \sigma\right)$$

$$+ \frac{1}{112}\sin\left(11\tau - \frac{\varepsilon_3}{2} - \varepsilon_4 - \sigma\right),$$

$$B_1 = -\frac{1}{64}\cos 2\sigma \cdot \sin\left(\tau - 2\varepsilon_1 + \frac{\varepsilon_3}{2} - \sigma\right) - \frac{1}{64}\sin 2\sigma \cdot \cos\left(\tau - 2\varepsilon_1 + \frac{\varepsilon_3}{2} - \sigma\right)$$

$$+ \frac{1}{640}\sin\left(7\tau - 2\varepsilon_1 - \frac{\varepsilon_3}{2} - \sigma\right),$$

$$B_2 = \frac{1}{128}\cos 2\sigma \cdot \sin\left(5\tau - 2\varepsilon_2 + \frac{\varepsilon_3}{2} - \sigma\right) + \frac{1}{128}\sin 2\sigma \cdot \cos\left(5\tau - 2\varepsilon_2 + \frac{\varepsilon_3}{2} - \sigma\right)$$

$$+ \frac{1}{4480}\sin\left(11\tau - 2\varepsilon_2 - \frac{\varepsilon_3}{2} - \sigma\right),$$

$$B_3 = \frac{1}{5184}\cos 2\sigma \cdot \sin\left(9\tau - \frac{3}{2}\varepsilon_3 - \sigma\right) + \frac{1}{1728}\sin 2\sigma \cdot \cos\left(9\tau - \frac{3}{2}\varepsilon_3 - \sigma\right)$$

$$+ \frac{1}{15552}\sin\left(15\tau - \frac{5}{2}\varepsilon_3 - \sigma\right),$$

$$B_4 = -\frac{1}{2560}\cos 2\sigma \cdot \sin\left(13\tau + \frac{\varepsilon_3}{2} - 2\varepsilon_4 - \sigma\right) - \frac{1}{2560}\sin 2\sigma \cdot \cos\left(13\tau + \frac{\varepsilon_3}{2} - 2\varepsilon_4 - \sigma\right)$$

$$+ \frac{1}{39424}\sin\left(19\tau - \frac{\varepsilon_3}{2} - 2\varepsilon_4 - \sigma\right),$$

$$B_{12} = \frac{1}{128}\sin\left(\tau - \varepsilon_1 + \varepsilon_2 - \frac{\varepsilon_3}{2} - \sigma\right) - \frac{1}{160}\sin\left(5\tau + \varepsilon_1 - \varepsilon_2 - \frac{\varepsilon_3}{2} - \sigma\right)$$

$$+ \frac{7}{5760}\sin\left(9\tau - \varepsilon_1 - \varepsilon_2 - \frac{\varepsilon_3}{2} - \sigma\right),$$

$$B_{13} = \frac{3}{128}\cos 2\sigma \cdot \sin\left(\tau + \varepsilon_1 - \frac{\varepsilon_3}{2} - \sigma\right) + \frac{5}{384}\sin 2\sigma \cdot \cos\left(\tau + \varepsilon_1 - \frac{\varepsilon_3}{2} - \sigma\right)$$

$$+ \frac{3}{256}\cos 2\sigma \cdot \sin\left(5\tau - \varepsilon_1 - \frac{\varepsilon_3}{2} - \sigma\right) + \frac{11}{768}\sin 2\sigma \cdot \cos\left(5\tau - \varepsilon_1 - \frac{\varepsilon_3}{2} - \sigma\right)$$

$$- \frac{1}{360}\sin\left(7\tau + \varepsilon_1 - \frac{3}{2}\varepsilon_3 - \sigma\right) + \frac{11}{16128}\sin\left(11\tau - \varepsilon_1 - \frac{3}{2}\varepsilon_3 - \sigma\right),$$

$$B_{14} = \frac{1}{640}\cos 2\sigma \cdot \sin\left(7\tau - \varepsilon_1 + \frac{\varepsilon_3}{2} - \varepsilon_4 - \sigma\right) + \frac{1}{640}\sin 2\sigma \cdot \cos\left(7\tau - \varepsilon_1 + \frac{\varepsilon_3}{2} - \varepsilon_4 - \sigma\right)$$

$$- \frac{13}{8064}\sin\left(9\tau + \varepsilon_1 - \frac{\varepsilon_3}{2} - \varepsilon_4 - \sigma\right) + \frac{1}{2240}\sin\left(13\tau - \varepsilon_1 - \frac{\varepsilon_3}{2} - \varepsilon_4 - \sigma\right),$$

$$B_{23} = -\left(\frac{1}{120} + \frac{1}{96}\cos 4\sigma\right)\sin\left(\tau - \varepsilon_2 + \frac{\varepsilon_3}{2} - \sigma\right) - \frac{1}{96}\sin 4\sigma\cdot\cos\left(\tau - \varepsilon_2 + \frac{\varepsilon_3}{2} - \sigma\right)$$

$$-\frac{1}{144}\sin\left(5\tau + \varepsilon_2 - \frac{3}{2}\varepsilon_3 - \sigma\right) + \frac{3}{800}\cos 2\sigma\cdot\sin\left(7\tau - \varepsilon_2 - \frac{\varepsilon_3}{2} - \sigma\right)$$

$$+\frac{11}{2400}\sin 2\sigma\cdot\cos\left(7\tau - \varepsilon_2 - \frac{\varepsilon_3}{2} - \sigma\right) + \frac{7}{28800}\sin\left(13\tau - \varepsilon_2 - \frac{3}{2}\varepsilon_3 - \sigma\right),$$

$$B_{24} = \frac{7}{640}\cos 2\sigma\cdot\sin\left(\tau + \varepsilon_2 + \frac{\varepsilon_3}{2} - \varepsilon_4 - \sigma\right) + \frac{7}{640}\sin 2\sigma\cdot\cos\left(\tau + \varepsilon_2 + \frac{\varepsilon_3}{2} - \varepsilon_4 - \sigma\right)$$

$$-\frac{13}{4480}\sin\left(7\tau + \varepsilon_2 - \frac{\varepsilon_3}{2} - \varepsilon_4 - \sigma\right) + \frac{1}{1152}\cos 2\sigma\cdot\sin\left(9\tau - \varepsilon_2 + \frac{\varepsilon_3}{2} - \varepsilon_4 - \sigma\right)$$

$$+\frac{1}{1152}\sin 2\sigma\cdot\cos\left(9\tau - \varepsilon_2 + \frac{\varepsilon_3}{2} - \varepsilon_4 - \sigma\right) + \frac{19}{120960}\sin\left(15\tau - \varepsilon_2 - \frac{\varepsilon_3}{2} - \varepsilon_4 - \sigma\right),$$

$$B_{34} = -\frac{11}{1152}\sin\left(\tau - \frac{3}{2}\varepsilon_3 + \varepsilon_4 - \sigma\right) + \left(\frac{5}{2688} - \frac{1}{192}\cos 4\sigma\right)\sin\left(5\tau + \frac{\varepsilon_3}{2} - \varepsilon_4 - \sigma\right)$$

$$-\frac{1}{192}\sin 4\sigma\cdot\cos\left(5\tau + \frac{\varepsilon_3}{2} - \varepsilon_4 - \sigma\right) - \frac{3}{6272}\cos 2\sigma\cdot\sin\left(11\tau - \frac{\varepsilon_3}{2} - \varepsilon_4 - \sigma\right)$$

$$-\frac{5}{18816}\sin 2\sigma\cdot\cos\left(11\tau - \frac{\varepsilon_3}{2} - \varepsilon_4 - \sigma\right) + \frac{23}{282240}\sin\left(17\tau - \frac{3}{2}\varepsilon_3 - \varepsilon_4 - \sigma\right).$$

APPENDIX IV

STABILITY CRITERION OF MANDELSTAM AND PAPALEXI

Stability investigations in non-linear oscillations are found in many physical and technical journals. The one reported by Mandelstam and Papalexi [21] with elegant form will be taken up here for comparison. They have discussed the subharmonic oscillations in vacuum tube circuits governed by the following equation, i.e.,

$$\frac{d^2v}{d\tau^2} + v = \lambda \cdot F\left(v, \frac{dv}{d\tau}\right) + B\cos\nu\tau, \qquad \nu = 2, 3, 4, \cdots, \qquad \text{(IV.1)}$$

in which the parametric coefficient λ of the non-linear function $F(v, dv/d\tau)$ is sufficiently small. They have treated the problem by the perturbation method, and obtained the following periodic solution for the subharmonic oscillation of order $1/\nu$, i.e.,

$$v(\tau) = x\sin\tau + y\cos\tau + w\cos\nu\tau, \qquad w = \frac{B}{1-\nu^2}, \qquad \text{(IV.2)}$$

in which the amplitudes x and y are determined by the conditions

$$\left.\begin{array}{l} \displaystyle\int_0^{2\pi} \psi(x, y, \tau)\sin\tau d\tau = 0, \\[2em] \displaystyle\int_0^{2\pi} \psi(x, y, \tau)\cos\tau d\tau = 0, \end{array}\right\} \qquad \text{(IV.3)}$$

where

$$\psi(x, y, \tau) = F(x\sin\tau + y\cos\tau + w\cos\nu\tau,$$
$$x\cos\tau - y\sin\tau - \nu w\sin\nu\tau).$$

This is quite the same relation as that obtained by substituting (IV.2) into (IV.1) and equating the coefficients of $\sin\tau$ and $\cos\tau$ separately to zero. Then, as for the stability condition, they have derived the relation

$$\begin{vmatrix} \displaystyle\int_0^{2\pi} \frac{\partial\psi}{\partial x}\sin\tau d\tau & \displaystyle\int_0^{2\pi} \frac{\partial\psi}{\partial x}\cos\tau d\tau \\[2em] \displaystyle\int_0^{2\pi} \frac{\partial\psi}{\partial y}\sin\tau d\tau & \displaystyle\int_0^{2\pi} \frac{\partial\psi}{\partial y}\cos\tau d\tau \end{vmatrix} > 0, \qquad \text{(IV.4)}$$

139

which has been deduced from the consideration that the variations of the amplitudes x and y of the subharmonic oscillation tend to zero with the lapse of time τ.

On the other hand, in our investigation, the differential equation which governs the oscillation is given by equation (5.1) in Section 5.1, in which the damping coefficient 2δ is constant, but not necessarily small. In order to investigate the subharmonic oscillations, the external force $e(\tau)$ may conveniently be expressed by $B \cos \nu\tau$, and then the periodic solution will be given by equation (IV. 2) (see Section 11).

Now we shall proceed to show that the stability condition (IV. 4) corresponds either to our condition (5. 5) for the first unstable region ($n = 1$) or to (5.7) for the second unstable region ($n = 2$).*

(1) We first consider the case in which the variational equation (5.3) leads to Hill's equation of the form (5.4). Then df/dv in (5.3) may be expanded in a Fourier series as

$$\frac{df}{dv} = a_0 + a_1 \cos 2\tau + a_2 \cos 4\tau + \cdots$$
$$+ b_1 \sin 2\tau + b_2 \sin 4\tau + \cdots,$$

where

$$\left. \begin{aligned} a_0 &= \frac{1}{2\pi} \int_0^{2\pi} \frac{df}{dv}\, d\tau, \\[2mm] a_\nu &= \frac{1}{\pi} \int_0^{2\pi} \frac{df}{dv} \cos 2\nu\tau d\tau, \qquad \nu = 1,\, 2,\, 3,\, \cdots, \\[2mm] b_\nu &= \frac{1}{\pi} \int_0^{2\pi} \frac{df}{dv} \sin 2\nu\tau d\tau, \qquad \nu = 1,\, 2,\, 3,\, \cdots. \end{aligned} \right\} \qquad \text{(IV. 5)}$$

Substituting this into (5.3), and comparing with (5.4), we obtain

$$\left. \begin{aligned} \theta_0 &= a_0 - \delta^2, \\[2mm] 2\theta_\nu &= \sqrt{a_\nu^2 + b_\nu^2}, \qquad \varepsilon_\nu = \arctan \frac{b_\nu}{a_\nu}. \end{aligned} \right\} \qquad \text{(IV. 6)}$$

Hence, the stability condition (5. 5) may be written as

$$(a_0 - n^2)^2 + 4n^2\delta^2 > \frac{1}{4}(a_n^2 + b_n^2),$$

---

* Which condition it will be depends on the non-linear characteristic and the order of the subharmonic oscillation (see Chapter IV).

and further, substitution for a_0, a_n, and b_n their values as given by (IV.5), leads to

$$\left[\int_0^{2\pi} \left(\frac{df}{dv} - n^2\right) d\tau\right]^2 + 16n^2\pi^2\delta^2 > \left[\int_0^{2\pi} \frac{df}{dv} \cos 2n\tau d\tau\right]^2 + \left[\int_0^{2\pi} \frac{df}{dv} \sin 2n\tau d\tau\right]^2,$$

or

$$\int_0^{2\pi} \left(\frac{df}{dv} - n^2\right) \sin^2 n\tau d\tau \cdot \int_0^{2\pi} \left(\frac{df}{dv} - n^2\right) \cos^2 n\tau d\tau$$

$$-\left[\int_0^{2\pi} \left(\frac{df}{dv} - n^2\right) \sin n\tau \cdot \cos n\tau d\tau\right]^2 + 4n^2\pi^2\delta^2 > 0.$$

This stability condition may be rewritten in a form similar to that of (IV.4) as

$$\left.\begin{array}{l} \begin{vmatrix} \displaystyle\int_0^{2\pi} \Psi_x \sin n\tau d\tau & \displaystyle\int_0^{2\pi} \Psi_x \cos n\tau d\tau \\[2em] \displaystyle\int_0^{2\pi} \Psi_y \sin n\tau d\tau & \displaystyle\int_0^{2\pi} \Psi_y \cos n\tau d\tau \end{vmatrix} > 0, \\[4em] \text{in which} \\[1em] \Psi_x = \left(\dfrac{df}{dv} - n^2\right) \sin n\tau + 2n\delta \cos n\tau, \\[2em] \Psi_y = \left(\dfrac{df}{dv} - n^2\right) \cos n\tau - 2n\delta \sin n\tau. \end{array}\right\} \quad \text{(IV.7)}$$

Now the stability condition (IV.4) may be derived by putting $n = 1$ in (IV.7), namely, upon comparing (IV.1) with (5.1), we have

$$\psi(x, y, \tau) = F\left(v, \frac{dv}{d\tau}\right) = \frac{1}{\lambda}\left[v - f(v) - 2\delta \frac{dv}{d\tau}\right],$$

and hence, by (IV.2),

$$\frac{\partial \psi}{\partial x} = \frac{1}{\lambda}\left(1 - \frac{df}{dv}\right) \sin \tau - \frac{2\delta}{\lambda} \cos \tau = -\frac{1}{\lambda}\left[\Psi_x\right]_{n=1},$$

$$\frac{\partial \psi}{\partial y} = \frac{1}{\lambda}\left(1 - \frac{df}{dv}\right) \cos \tau + \frac{2\delta}{\lambda} \sin \tau = -\frac{1}{\lambda}\left[\Psi_y\right]_{n=1}.$$

The substitution of these two relations into (IV.7) will yield (IV.4).

Therefore, the stability condition given by Mandelstam and Papalexi offers no information for $n \geq 2$. This is because they have discussed the problem by the perturbation method, assuming that the non-linear term $\lambda \cdot F(v, dv/d\tau)$ in

(IV.1) is sufficiently small. Whereas, in our investigation, the generalized stability condition (5.5) for the nth unstable region will furnish the criterion to distinguish the stability for the nth harmonic of the fundamental oscillation. Thus, for example, when we discuss the subharmonic oscillation of order 1/3, the stability condition takes the form of equation (5.5), and it was concluded in Section 12.2 that the condition (5.5) for $n=2$ as well as for $n=1$ must be considered in the case when the non-linearity is characterized by a quintic function. Therefore, the stability condition of Mandelstam and Papalexi is not sufficient in this case.

(2) We have still another case in which the variational equation (5.3) leads to Hill's equation of the form (5.6). Proceeding similarly as in the foregoing case, we may finally conclude that the stability condition of Mandelstam and Papalexi is obtained from our condition (5.7) by putting $n=2$. In the case of the subharmonic oscillation of order 1/2, the stability condition leads to equation (5.7), and the condition for the nth unstable region ascertains the stability against building up of the unstable oscillation of order $n/4$. As explained in Section 13.1 (c), the unstable oscillations not only of order 1/2 (*viz.*, $n=2$) but also of orders 1/4, 3/4 actually take place under certain circumstances, so that the condition (IV.4) is not sufficient in this case too.

Summarizing the preceding two cases, it may be concluded that the condition (IV.4) of Mandelstam and Papalexi will only ascertain the stability against building up of the unstable oscillation whose period is the same as that of the fundamental oscillation $x \sin \tau + y \cos \tau$ in equation (IV.2), and tells no more on the building up of the oscillations of different orders.

APPENDIX V

REMARKS CONCERNING INTEGRAL CURVES AND SINGULAR POINTS

(a) Integral curves in the neighborhood of a singular point

In Part II we have treated the system of two differential equations of the first order, namely

$$\left.\begin{aligned}
\frac{dx}{d\tau} &= X(x,\,y) = a_1 x + a_2 y + X_2\,(x,\,y)\,, \\[2mm]
\frac{dy}{d\tau} &= Y(x,\,y) = b_1 x + b_2 y + Y_2\,(x,\,y)\,,
\end{aligned}\right\} \tag{V.1}$$

where X_2, Y_2 are polynomials containing terms of higher degree than the first. Since the right-hand sides of equations (V.1) vanish for $x = y = 0$, the origin is a singular point. We shall here confine our attention to the integral curves in the neighborhood of the origin. Then, instead of (V.1), we may deal with*

$$\left.\begin{aligned}
\frac{dx}{d\tau} &= a_1 x + a_2 y\,, \\[2mm]
\frac{dy}{d\tau} &= b_1 x + b_2 y\,,
\end{aligned}\right\} \tag{V.2}$$

from which, by eliminating τ, we obtain

$$\frac{dy}{dx} = \frac{b_1 x + b_2 y}{a_1 x + a_2 y}\,. \tag{V.3}$$

We may easily integrate this by a well-known procedure for homogeneous equations. We thus obtain

$$(y - \mu_1 x)^{\lambda_1}(y - \mu_2 x)^{-\lambda_2} = \text{const.},$$

where

$$\left.\begin{aligned}
\lambda_1 &= \frac{a_1 + b_2 + \sqrt{(a_1 - b_2)^2 + 4 a_2 b_1}}{2}\,, \\[3mm]
\lambda_2 &= \frac{a_1 + b_2 - \sqrt{(a_1 - b_2)^2 + 4 a_2 b_1}}{2}\,,
\end{aligned}\right\} \tag{V.4}$$

---

* We exclude certain special cases which will be mentioned in the following paragraph.

$$\mu_1 = \frac{-(a_1-b_2)+\sqrt{(a_1-b_2)^2+4a_2b_1}}{2a_2},$$

$$\mu_2 = \frac{-(a_1-b_2)-\sqrt{(a_1-b_2)^2+4a_2b_1}}{2a_2}.$$

However, it is assumed here that λ_1, λ_2 are neither zero nor equal and further that $a_2 \neq 0$.

Now we see that λ_1 and λ_2 are the characteristic roots of equation (15.8) [see equations (16.3)]. As mentioned in Section 16, the singularity (i.e., the origin in this case) is classified into 4 types, namely, the node, the saddle, the spiral, and the center according to the values of λ_1 and λ_2. In the case when the singularity is a node or a saddle point, μ_1 and μ_2 show the tangential direction of the integral curves at the singularity. For, if we denote the tangential direction by μ, then

$$\mu = \left(\frac{dy}{dx}\right)_{\substack{x=0,\\y=0}} = \lim_{\substack{x\to0,\\y\to0}} \frac{y}{x},$$

and substituting this into (V.3), we get the relations given by the last two equations of (V.4).

It is added here that if, in particular, $(a_1-b_2)^2+4a_2b_1 = 0$ in equation (V.3), we have $\lambda_1 = \lambda_2$, $\mu_1 = \mu_2$, and, instead of (V.4), the solution becomes

$$\log\left[(a_1-b_2)x+2a_2y\right] = \frac{(a_1+b_2)x}{(a_1-b_2)x+2a_2y} + \text{const.}, \tag{V.5}$$

and if $a_2 = 0$, the solution is

$$\left[b_1x + (b_2-a_1)y\right] x^{-\frac{b_2}{a_1}} = \text{const.} \tag{V.6}$$

In the case when the singularity is a spiral point, λ and μ in (V.4) are complex numbers, and it may be expedient to express the integral curves in polar coordinates, thus:

$$x = r\cos\theta, \qquad y = r\sin\theta.$$

Then equation (V.3) becomes

$$\frac{1}{r}\frac{dr}{d\theta} = \frac{a_1\cos^2\theta+(a_2+b_1)\sin\theta\cos\theta+b_2\sin^2\theta}{b_1\cos^2\theta+(b_2-a_1)\sin\theta\cos\theta-a_2\sin^2\theta}. \tag{V.7}$$

Integrating this, we obtain

$$r = \frac{C \cdot e^{M \arctan G}}{\sqrt{b_1 \cos^2 \theta + (b_2 - a_1) \sin \theta \cos \theta - a_2 \sin^2 \theta}},$$

where

$$M = \frac{a_1 + b_2}{\sqrt{-D}}, \qquad G = \frac{-2a_2 \tan \theta - a_2 + b_2}{\sqrt{-D}},$$

$$D = (a_1 - b_2)^2 + 4a_2 b_1 \; (<0),$$

(V.8)

C being an arbitrary constant.

The integral curves spiral around the origin, and for each revolution the change in r is determined by

$$r(\theta + 2\pi) = e^{\sigma \cdot 2\pi M} \cdot r(\theta), \qquad (V.9)$$

where σ is $+1$ or -1 according as $a_2 < 0$ or $a_2 > 0$. Further, from (V.2) we obtain

$$\frac{d\theta}{d\tau} = \frac{1}{2} \Big[(b_1 - a_2) + (a_2 + b_1) \cos 2\theta + (b_2 - a_1) \sin 2\theta \Big].$$

As the singularity is of the spiral type, we have

$$(a_1 - b_2)^2 + 4a_2 b_1 < 0,$$

or

$$(b_1 - a_2)^2 > (a_2 + b_1)^2 + (b_2 - a_1)^2,$$

so that $d\theta/d\tau$ has the same sign as that of $b_1 - a_2$. Since a_2 and b_1 are of opposite signs, it is concluded that

$$1^0. \quad \text{if} \quad a_2 > 0 \text{ (or } b_1 < 0), \quad \text{then} \quad \frac{d\theta}{d\tau} < 0,$$

$$2^0. \quad \text{if} \quad a_2 < 0 \text{ (or } b_1 > 0), \quad \text{then} \quad \frac{d\theta}{d\tau} > 0.$$

(V.10)

Thus it follows that when $a_2 > 0$, a point (r, θ) moves, with the increase of τ, on the integral curve in the clockwise direction and tends to the singular point if $e^{-2\pi M} > 1$ or $a_1 + b_2 < 0$. Hence the singular point is stable in this case. Other possible cases may be treated in like manner.

(b) Classification of the singular point of equations (V.1)

Following the classification given in Section 16, the type of a singularity will be definite when the characteristic roots λ_1 and λ_2 are neither zero nor pure imaginary and when they are distinct. Now, in this paragraph, we shall see the special cases which have not been explicitly referred to.

We consider first the case in which $(a_1-b_2)^2+4a_2b_1 = 0$. The roots λ_1 and λ_2 are then real and equal. Although the detailed discussion is omitted here,* the corresponding singularity is still a nodal point in this particular case. An example for such a case was given in Section 18.2 (a).

Further it will be noticed that the condition $a_1+b_2 = 0$ is not sufficient to distinguish between a center and a spiral in the case when $(a_1-b_2)^2+4a_2b_1 < 0$, and that the higher order terms $X_2(x, y)$, $Y_2(x, y)$ in (V.1) must be taken into account for this purpose.† This case has actually occured in the investigation in Section 18.1. Fortunately, however, the differential equation was integrable in that case, and we could in fact see that the singularity was a center.

Thus far we have dealt with the singularity which is simple, or in other words, of the first kind. As mentioned in Sections 18.1 (b) and 18.2 (b), however, we have also the singularity of the second kind for which either or both roots of the characteristic equation are zero. We have at least one zero root if one of the following conditions is satisfied, i. e. [see equation (V.1)],

$$a_1 = a_2 = 0, \quad b_1 = b_2 = 0, \quad \text{and} \quad a_1/a_2 = b_1/b_2 . \qquad (V.11)$$

When $a_1 = a_2 = 0$ (or $b_1 = b_2 = 0$) the curve $X(x, y) = 0$ [or $Y(x, y) = 0$] has the origin (i. e., the singularity) for multiple point; and when $a_1/a_2 = b_1/b_2$ the curves $X(x, y) = 0$ and $Y(x, y) = 0$ have a common tangent at the origin.

The detailed discussion of the singularities of the second kind has already been given in Section 18.2 (b) where one root of the characteristic equation is zero, and in Section 18.1 (b) where both roots are zero.

(c) The following theorems‡ are due to Bendixson and quoted in our investigation of integral curves in Part II.

1⁰. First theorem of Bendixson

We consider the system of differential equations

$$\begin{rcases} \dfrac{dx}{d\tau} = X_m + X_{m+1} , \\[2mm] \dfrac{dy}{d\tau} = Y_m + Y_{m+1} , \end{rcases} \qquad (V.12)$$

---

* For a rigorous treatment, see the paper by Bendixson [3, p. 50].
† Poincaré [48, p. 95] has shown a criterion for distinguishing these two types.
‡ For the proofs see the paper by Bendixson [3, pp. 34, 45].

where X_m and Y_m are polynomials which are homogeneous and of degree m in x, y, and X_{m+1}, Y_{m+1} are holomorphic functions containing terms of degree $> m$.

The theorem of Bendixson then states that the integral curves of the system (V.12) tend to the origin (1) without any definite direction, thus in the manner of spirals, or (2) with the definite direction determined by the equation

$$x Y_m - y X_m = 0 . \tag{V.13}$$

2^0. Second theorem of Bendixson

We deal with the differential equation

$$x^m \frac{dy}{dx} = ay + bx + B(x, y), \tag{V.14}$$

where $B(x, y)$ is a holomorphic function containing terms of degree ≥ 2 in x, y, and assume that $a \neq 0$.

Bendixson has derived the following conclusions.

Case 1. $a > 0$, m: even number

There is one and only one branch of the integral curve tending to the origin on the left side of the y-axis, while the integral curves on the other side constitute a nodal distribution (i. e., they form a nodal region for $x > 0$). These integral curves are schematically illustrated in Fig. V.1.

Case 2. $a < 0$, m: even number

By the substitution $x = -x'$, this case is reduced to the preceding one, thus we have a nodal distribution for $x < 0$, and a saddle distribution for $x > 0$.

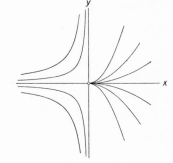

Fig. V.1. Coalescence of node with saddle.

Case 3. $a > 0$, m: odd number

The origin is a nodal point.

Case 4. $a < 0$, m: odd number

The origin is a saddle point.

APPENDIX VI

ELECTRONIC SYNCHRONOUS SWITCH

As mentioned in Sections 20 and 22, we used an electronic synchronous switch in order to prescribe the initial condition θ_0, i.e., the phase angle of the applied voltage at which the circuit was closed. An ordinary mechanical switch (timed mechanically or even electronically) is not adequate for this purpose, since it has a time lag which is not constant for all operations.

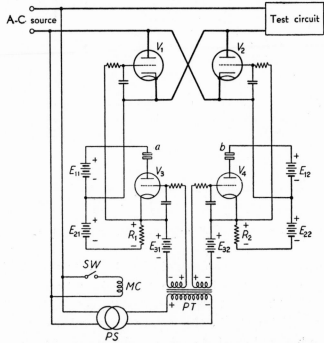

V_1, V_2: main thyratron tubes V_3, V_4: thyratron tubes for control
PT: peaking transformer PS: phase shifter MC: magnetic relay

FIG. VI. 1. Connection diagram of the electronic switch.

Figure VI.1 shows the circuit diagram of the electronic switch used in our experiments. The main tubes V_1 and V_2 are thyratrons connected in inverse-parallel, thus allowing the alternating current to flow in both directions. These tubes are electronically controlled by the auxiliary thyratrons V_3 and V_4 incorporated with the peaking transformer PT and the phase shifter PS.

The sequence of operation is as follows: first the manual switch SW is open. Then the magnetic relay MC is not energized, and its contacts a, b are also open. Hence, the tubes V_3 and V_4 are non-conductive. Since no currents are flowing through the resistors R_1 and R_2, there are no voltage drops across R_1 and R_2, and the grids of V_1 and V_2 are kept negative by the d–c biases E_{21} and E_{22} respectively. Hence, the tubes V_1 and V_2 are also blocked.*

Next, suppose the switch SW is closed at the instant marked in Fig. VI. 2 a. Then the relay MC is energized and the contacts a, b close; but this would

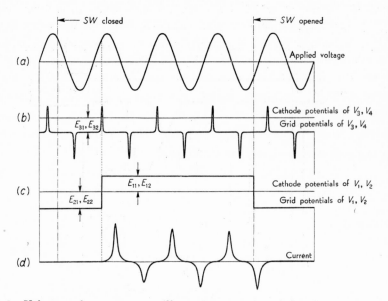

FIG. VI. 2. Voltage and current waves illustrating operation of the electronic switch.

not give rise to the simultaneous firing of V_3 and V_4. These tubes break down at the instant the positive peaks (from the peaking transformer PT) are impressed on their grids against the d–c biases E_{31} and E_{32} (see Fig. VI. 2 b). After break-down of V_3 and V_4, the voltage drops which develop across R_1 and R_2 exceed the biases E_{21} and E_{22} respectively, and render the grid voltages of V_1 and V_2 positive as illustrated in Fig. VI. 2 c. Consequently V_1 and V_2 fire alternately with the alternation of the main current. An example of the wave form of the main current is illustrated in Fig. VI. 2 d.

---

* The thyratron fires (under positive anode voltage) when the grid voltage is raised over the critical grid voltage, and after conduction starts, it cannot be stopped or influenced by grid control. Conduction can be stopped only by reducing the current to zero long enough for the tube to deionize. During conduction the arc drop, about 10 volts in our case, is only slightly affected by a change of current within the operating range.

We thus see that, regardless of the time of closure of the manual switch *SW*, the main alternating current always starts at a predetermined phase angle (i. e., θ_0) on the voltage wave as determined by the instant at which the peaked positive voltages are impressed on the grids of V_3 and V_4. This phase angle may arbitrarily be prescribed by the setting of the phase shifter *PS* which energizes the peaking transformer *PT*.

It is also mentioned that when the manual switch *SW* is opened, the relay *MC* is de-energized, and the contacts a, b open, stopping the firing of V_3 and V_4, and simultaneously impressing the negative biases on the grids of V_1 and V_2, but the discharge continues until the end of that half cycle (see Fig. VI. 2 d).

The accuracy of timing of the electronic synchronous switch is determined by the ionization time of the thyratrons as well as the error in indication of the phase shifter. The former is of the order of 10 microseconds which correspond to 0.2 degree in phase angle* (one cycle of a–c voltage corresponding to 360 degrees), and the latter may be kept within 0.3 degree if the phase shifter is carefully constructed in this respect. Consequently the total error in the phase angle θ_0 may be less than 0.5 degree.

---

* The supply frequency is 60 c. p. s.

REFERENCES

A. SCIENTIFIC PAPERS

1. Andronow, A., and A. Witt. Zur Theorie des Mitnehmens von van der Pol. Arch. Elektrotech. **24**, 99, 1930.

2. Appleton, E. V., and B. van der Pol. On a type of oscillation-hysteresis in a simple triode generator. Phil. Mag. **6-43**, 177, 1922.

3. Bendixson, I. Sur les courbes définies par des équations différentielles. Acta Mathematica, **24**, 1, 1901.

4. Cartwright, M. L. Non-linear Vibrations. Advancement of Science, **6**, April, 1949.

5. Floquet, G. Sur les équations différentielles linéaires. Ann. de l'École Norm. Sup. **2-12**, 47, 1883.

6. Goldstein, S. Mathieu functions. Trans. Cambridge Phil. Soc. **23**, 303, 1927.

7. Hayashi, C. Studies on low frequency oscillations in transformer circuits. Elec. Rev. (Kyoto Univ.) **29**, 599, 670, 732, 1941; **30**, 418, 479, 551, 597, 1942 (in Japanese).

8. Hayashi, C. Subharmonic oscillations. Mitsubishi Denki, **18**, 128, 1942 (in Japanese).

9. Hayashi, C. Periodic oscillations and their stability in a non-linear oscillatory circuit with saturable iron-core. J. Inst. Elec. Engrs. of Japan, Tech. Pap. 4, 161, 1943 (in Japanese).

10. Hayashi, C. Forced oscillations with nonlinear restoring force. J. Appl. Phys. **24**, 198, 1953.

11. Hayashi, C. Stability investigation of the nonlinear periodic oscillations. J. Appl. Phys. **24**, 344, 1953.

12. Hayashi, C. Subharmonic oscillations in nonlinear systems. J. Appl. Phys. **24**, 521, 1953.

13. Hill, G. W. On the part of the motion of the lunar perigee. Acta Mathematica, 8, 1, 1886.

14. Hurwitz, A. Über die Bedingungen, unter welchen eine Gleichung nur Wurzeln mit negativen reellen Teilen besitzt. Math. Ann. **46**, 273, 1895.

15. Ince, E. L. On a general solution of Hill's equation. Monthly Notices Roy. Astron. Soc. **75**, 436, 1915; **76**, 431, 1916; **78**, 141, 1917.

16. Ince, E. L. Researches into the characteristic numbers of the Mathieu equation. Proc. Roy. Soc. Edinburgh, **46**, 20, 316, 1925-26; **47**, 294, 1926-27.

17. Ince, E. L. Tables of the elliptic-cylinder functions. Proc. Roy. Soc. Edinburgh, **52**, 355, 1931-32.

18. Jeffreys, H. On certain approximate solutions of Mathieu's equation. Proc. London Math. Soc. **23**, 437, 1924.

19. Liapounoff, M. A. Problème général de la stabilité du mouvement. Annales de la Faculté des Sci. de Toulouse, **9**, 203, 1907.

20. Liénard, A. Étude des oscillations entretenues. Rev. Gén. de l'Élec. **23**, 901, 946, 1928.

21 Mandelstam, L., and N. Papalexi. Über Resonanzerscheinungen bei Frequenzteilung. Z. Physik, **73**, 223, 1932.

22. Mathieu, É. Mémoire sur le mouvement vibratoire d'une membrane de forme elliptique. Jour. de Math. **2-13**, 137, 1868.

23. McCrumm, J. D. Experimental investigation of subharmonic currents. Trans. Am. Inst. Elec. Engrs. **60**, 533, 1941.

24. Pedersen, P. O. Subharmonics in forced oscillations in dissipative systems. J. Acoust. Soc. Am. **6**, 227, 1935; **7**, 64, 1935.

25. Poincaré, H. Sur les courbes définies par une équation différentielle. Jour. de Math. **3-7**, 375, 1881; **3-8**, 251, 1882.

26. Poincaré, H. Sur les courbes définies par les équations différentielles. Jour. de Math. **4-1**, 167, 1885; **4-2**, 151, 1886.

27. Pol, B. van der. On relaxation-oscillations. Phil. Mag. **7-2**, 978, 1926.

28. Pol, B. van der. Forced oscillations in a circuit with non-linear resistance. Phil. Mag. **7-3**, 65, 1927.

29. Pol, B. van der. and M. J. O. Strutt. On the stability of the solutions of Mathieu's equation. Phil. Mag. **7-5**, 18, 1928.

30. Pol, B. van der. Nonlinear theory of electric oscillations. Proc. Inst. Radio Engrs. **22**, 1051, 1934.

31. Rouelle, E. Contribution à l'étude expérimentale de la ferro-résonance. Rev. Gén. de l'Élec. **36**, 715, 763, 795, 841, 1934.

32. Rüdenberg, R. Nonharmonic oscillations as caused by magnetic saturation. Trans. Am. Inst. Elec. Engrs. **68**, 676, 1949.

33. Trefftz, E. Zu den Grundlagen der Schwingungstheorie. Math. Ann. **95**, 307, 1926.

34. Wada, T. Graphical solution of $dy/dx = f(x, y)$. Memoirs of the College of Science, Kyoto Imp. Univ. **2**, 151, 1917.

35. Watson, G. N. Convergence of series for Mathieu functions. Proc. Edinburgh Math. Soc. **33**, 25, 1914-15.

36. Whittaker, E. T. General solution of Mathieu's equation. Proc. Edinburgh Math. Soc. **32**, 75, 1913-14.

37. Young, A. W. Quasi-periodic solutions of Mathieu's equation. Proc. Edinburgh Math. Soc. **32**, 81, 1913-14.

B. BOOKS AND REPORTS

38. Andronow, A. A., and C. E. Chaikin. Theory of Oscillations. English translation edited by S. Lefschetz (Princeton, 1949).

39. Duffing, G. Erzwungene Schwingungen bei veränderlicher Eigenfrequenz und ihre technische Bedeutung (Sammlung Vieweg, Braunschweig, 1918).

40. Kryloff, N., and N. Bogoliuboff. Introduction to Non-linear Mechanics. Translated from the Russian by S. Lefschetz (Annals of Mathematics Studies No. 11, Princeton, 1947).

41. Lefschetz, S. Contributions to the Theory of Nonlinear Oscillations (Annals of Mathematics Studies No. 20, Princeton, 1950).

42. Liapounoff, M. A. Problème Général de la Stabilité du Mouvement (Annals of Mathematics Studies No. 17, Princeton, 1949).

43. Lowan, A. N., and others. Tables Relating to Mathieu Functions (Computation Lab., National Bureau of Standards, U. S. A., 1951).

44. Mathieu, É. Cours de Physique Mathematique (Gauthier-Villars, 1873).

45. McLachlan, N. W. Theory and Application of Mathieu Functions (Oxford, 1947).

46. McLachlan, N. W. Ordinary Non-linear Differential Equations (Oxford, 1950).

47. Minorsky, N. Introduction to Non-linear Mechanics (J. W. Edwards, Ann Arbor, U. S. A., 1947).

48. Poincaré, H. Œuvres, Vol. 1 (Gauthier-Villars, Paris, 1928).

49. Rayleigh, Lord. Theory of Sound, Vol. 1 (Macmillan, London, 1894).

50. Routh, E. J. Dynamics of a System of Rigid Bodies, Advanced Part (Macmillan, London, 1892).

51. Stoker, J. J. Nonlinear Vibrations (Interscience Publishers, New York, 1950).

52. Strutt, M. J. O. Lamésche, Mathieusche, und verwandte Funktionen in Physik und Technik (Ergebnisse der Mathematik und ihrer Grenzgebiete, 1-3, Springer, 1932).

53. Whittaker, E. T., and G. N. Watson. A Course of Modern Analysis (Cambridge, 1935).

INDEX

157